ALFRED NORTH WHITEHEAD'S EARLY PHILOSOPHY OF SPACE AND TIME

Janet A. Fitzgerald, O.P., PH.D.

D1593170

0146731

University Press
of America™

Copyright © 1979 by

University Press of America, Inc.™

4710 Auth Place, S.E., Washington D.C. 20023

ISBN: 0-8191-0747-6

Library of Congress Catalog Card Number: 79-63849

ALFRED NORTH WHITEHEAD'S

EARLY PHILOSOPHY OF SPACE AND TIME

BY

JANET A. FITZGERALD, O.P.,PH.D.

UNIVERSITY PRESS OF AMERICA

WASHINGTON, D.C.

ACKNOWLEDGEMENTS

Every work of this kind reflects to a great extent not only the efforts and thinking of the author but also the inspiration, guidance, and encouragement she has received from others. Therefore, it is important that I take this opportunity to recognize publicly and express my gratitude to my professors of philosophy and mathematics at St. John's University. The translation of Whitehead's address, "La Theorie Relationniste de l'Espace," was accomplished with the assistance of one of my Dominican Sisters and colleague at Molloy College, Sister Marie Albertina Oyarbide, Ph.D. To Kathryn Conroy, formerly manager of Sheed and Ward and a close friend, my sincerest thanks for urging me to take time out from my presidential duties to publish this work and for her hours of professional expertise in preparing the manuscript.

Finally, my most grateful appreciation to the renowned scholar and philosopher of science, Dr. Ernest Nagel, Professor Emeritus of the faculty of Philosophy of Columbia University for his kindness, encouragement, and interest in this work.

The author gratefully acknowledges permission to quote material from the following publications:

Cambridge University Press, New York, New York., "An Enquiry Concerning the Principles of Natural Knowledge" by Alfred North Whitehead and "The Concept of Nature" by Alfred North Whitehead.

MacMillan Publishing Co., Inc. New York, N.Y., "The Aims of Education and Other Essays" by Alfred North Whitehead, and "Process and Reality" by Alfred North Whitehead.

Robert Palter, Ph.D., University of Texas at Austin and the University of Chicago Press, Chicago, Illinois, "Whitehead's Philosophy of Science" by Robert Palter.

FOREWORD

Though the problems of space and time have received the attention of philosophers throughout the course of the centuries, there can be no doubt that Einstein's theories of special and general relativity caused a renewal of interest in the relation of sensed time and sensed space with the space-time manifold demanded by contemporary physics. It was a rude awakening to discover that our familiar, common-sense notions of space and time were suddenly inadequate to fit the experimental facts, and this shock triggered a critical attitude toward our whole conceptual structure. Among the twentieth-century philosophers who have attempted a theory of space-time which would "fit the philosophy to the science" is Alfred North Whitehead, renowned logician, mathematician, and philosopher. Whitehead's solution to the problem, the method of extensive abstraction, constitutes his major contribution to the philosophy of science. The method was not a sudden inspiration, but was laboriously developed and carefully revised over a period of twenty-five years of Whitehead's career. Very little work has been done by philosophers interested in Whitehead in tracing the genesis and growth of Whitehead's crucial doctrine of space and time. Was his method of extensive abstraction of space and time a success in accomplishing its goals of reconstructing the bases of mathematics and science in accordance with our sense perception? This is the burning issue debated by the philosophers of science.

We can point out three major critics of Whitehead's philosophy of space and time as culminated in the method of extensive abstraction. They are V.F. Lenzen, Adolf Grünbaum, and Ernest Nagel - all prominent and respected scholars. Yet, each one of these has been responded to by at least one of Whitehead's defenders giving us the material for three major debates on the subject: the Lenzen-Murphy Debate, the Grunbaum - Mays Debate, and the Nagel-Lowe Debate. The core of the debates centers about two main issues: (1) the correspondence between perceived entities and mathematical entities: the former supposedly inexact and vague;

vii

the latter exact and definite, and (2) the validity (or invalidity) of the use of mathematical concepts such as infinity and convergence to a limit in a conceptual instrument which is to derive scientific entities from observable entities.

By examining further the suggestions offered by Wolfe Mays and Victor Lowe that Whitehead's method is an empirically based mathematical model. I believe a resolution to the debates is possible. However, to do this, much more attention must be paid to the development of Whitehead's early writings on the problem of space and time as well as his theory of sense perception. Thus, this book will trace Whitehead's method of extensive abstraction from its origins in the "Memoir of 1905" and "La Theorie Relationniste de l'Espace" through the refinements and revisions made in Process and Reality. The two earlier works of Whitehead have been relatively unanalyzed by scholars. For that reason I have included as an appendix to this book my translation of "La Theorie", a work which is not only very difficult to obtain in the original French but to my knowledge has never been translated in published form. A close scrutiny will result in a clearer understanding of Whitehead's method of extensive abstraction as a mathematical model.

If Whitehead's treatment of space and time is truly a mathematical model in the contemporary sense of the term, it must fulfill certain requirements. The fundamental requirement of such a model is that it must possess the property of isomorphism. An isomorphism displays similarity of structure between the two fields of comparison by setting up a one-to-one correspondence between the entities and relations of both fields. If it can be shown that "perceived" natural entities possess exactness and definiteness in Whitehead's theory of perception, then the correspondence between these "perceived" entities and the "mathematical" entities of the method of extensive abstraction is easily demonstrated. The method is then accurately judged a "mathematical model." However, it must be shown that perception for Whitehead does indeed endow the fragmentary sense data with this definiteness and exactness. For this purpose, the second step of this study is a detailed study of Whitehead's early perceptual theory up to 1924.

However, even if a critic demands that in order for Whitehead's method to be true to his original wishes,

viii

the isomorphism must be set up between the mathematical entities of the method and the natural entities _per se_ (and not the natural entities as "perceived"), it can still be shown that Whitehead's method of extensive abstraction remains a mathematical model because it fulfills several functions of models. In this latter case, the method is an "approximative isomorphism." This judgment is based on an appeal to contemporary literature on the philosophy of the scientific model - the third and final step of this study.

The conclusion yielded by this three-stepped procedure is that, indeed, Whitehead's method of extensive abstraction from its origins in 1905 through its final, metaphysical appearance in _Process and Reality_, is a mathematical model. As such, Whitehead is cleared of many of the charges of his critics who claim that he used mathematical principles invalidly. The major issues of the Lenzen-Murphy, Grunbaum-Mays, Nagel-Lowe Debates are thus satisfactorily resolved, and the worth of Whitehead's philosophy of space and time in the philosophy of science is recognized as a major contribution in bridging the gap between the level of sense observation and the level of theoretical science.

CONTENTS

xi

CONTENTS (continued)

Chapter   Page

CONTENTS (continued)

LIST OF ILLUSTRATIONS

LIST OF ABBREVIATIONS

The more frequently cited works of Alfred North Whitehead are usually abbreviated in the notes as follows. The year of first publication is given, but in all cases the edition referred to in the dissertation is that given in the bibliography.

AE   The Aims of Education and Other Essays (1929)

AI   Adventures of Ideas (1933)

CN   The Concept of Nature (1920)

ESP   Essays in Science and Philosophy (1947)

IS   The Interpretation of Science: Selected Essays, Ed. A. H. Johnson, 1947.

MC   "On Mathematical Concepts of the Material World" (1906)

PM   Principia Mathematica, 3 Vols. (1910-1913)

PNK   An Enquiry Concerning the Principles of Natural Knowledge (1919)

PR   Process and Reality (1929)

PRel   The Principle of Relativity with Applications to Physical Science (1922)

RTS   "La Theorie Relationniste de l'Espace" (1914)

SMW   Science and the Modern World (1925)

Sym   Symbolism, Its Meaning and Effect (1928)

UA   A Treatise on Universal Algebra, with Applications (1898)

CHAPTER I

THE MAN AND HIS WORK

The name of Alfred North Whitehead is known
in varying degrees by college students everywhere. Some
know him for his writings on education. Others know of
his pioneering in what is called "process philosophy".
Mathematics and logic students link him to the monumental task of reducing mathematics to logic, a task which
he and Bertrand Russell undertook in Principia
Mathematica. Metaphysics students grapple with his bi-
polar God of becoming while philosophers of science
marvel at his advanced theory of relativity. Yet,
though his name is almost commonplace in the American
and English universities, very few know the great scope
of Whitehead's endeavors nor the greatness which he
achieved as a mathematician, physicist, educator, meta-
physician and beloved professor. It is worth our time
to survey briefly the life and intellectual interests
of Whitehead before we delve deeply into his theory of
space and time.

Alfred North Whitehead was born on February
15, 1861, in Kent, England, of a family of educators and
clergymen. His grandfather and father were school-
masters, but his father, Alfred Whitehead, abandoned his
teaching career for the life of an Anglican clergyman.

At fourteen Whitehead attended Sherborne, one
of England's oldest, most historic schools which dates
from the eighth century and claims Alfred the Great as
one of its most distinguished alumni. The curriculum
at Sherborne was predominantly classical, and it was here
that the young Whitehead became steeped in Latin, Greek,
and history. The Romantic poets, Wordsworth and Shelley,
were his favorite selections for private reading. Whitehead's classical training never left him but was
cultivated for the remainder of his life. In an age
when scientists and humanists are presumed to possess
distinct personalities, it was a common saying that
"Whitehead has both."(1)

1

Whitehead's university career began in the autumn of 1880 at Trinity College, Cambridge. Since it was the policy of Cambridge to allow each undergraduate to study only a narrow subject range, Whitehead attended formal lectures covering only pure and applied mathematics. This is not to imply that his education was so extremely specialized as to exclude other fields. As he himself states, these lectures formed but one small part of his education. Perhaps the most rewarding feature of his student years at Cambridge was the broad knowledge gleaned from discussion with his companions:

> Groups of friends were not created by
> identity of subjects for study. We all came
> from the same sort of school, with the same
> sort of previous training. We discussed
> everything--politics, religion, philosophy,
> literature--with a bias toward literature.
> This experience led to a large amount of
> miscellaneous reading.(2)

In the autumn of 1885, Whitehead was awarded a fellowship and teaching position at Trinity where he taught mathematics for the next twenty-five years. In December 1890, Whitehead married a most remarkable woman, Evelyn Willoughby Wade, the daughter of an Irish military family. Whitehead writes of their marriage:

> The effect of my wife upon my outlook on
> the world has been so fundamental, that it must
> be mentioned as an essential factor in my
> philosophical outlook . . . Her vivid life has
> taught me that beauty, moral and aesthetic, is
> the aim of existence; and that kindness, and
> love, and artistic satisfaction are among its
> modes of attainment.

The marriage was blessed with two sons, North and Eric, and a daughter Jessie. All three served in World War I, and Eric, an aviator, was killed when his plane was shot down over France. This loss was a great one for Whitehead--one which could never be fathomed by those outside the family circle:

> Only as one came to know them gradually year
> after year did one even remotely understand
> how Eric's loss was felt. Finally they could
> talk of him eagerly and with laughter, but
> Whitehead once said that the most vivid

wordings of grief or attempts at consolation
by those masters of speech, the English poets,
to him "only trivialized the actual emotions."

In 1910 the Whiteheads moved to London.
After three years at the University of London, Whitehead was awarded a professorship. During his fourteen
years at London, Whitehead's views on the problem of
higher education in modern civilization were transformed.
Also, Whitehead's philosophical writings began in
London--the London Aristotelian Society providing a
center for discussion and the forming of friendships.
In 1924, at the age of 63, Whitehead accepted unhesi-
tatingly an invitation to join the Philosophy Faculty
at Harvard University. In a new land he began what was
by far the most productive and brilliant part of his
career. Though it was expected that he would write and
not do much teaching, Whitehead did both. He not only
lectured three times weekly but dedicated the entire
afternoon or evening on those days to his students. For
thirteen years students spent weekly "evenings at the
Whiteheads'" where conversation and discussion
flourished. His influence on students remained quite
strong up until the time of his death when the editor of
"The Crimson" wrote of him:

He teaches no dogma . . . but achieves
an ignition between mind and mind . . . such
that the torch lives on . . . as indestructible
as philosophy itself.(3)

On December 30, 1947, Whitehead died in his
small apartment near Harvard Yard, but as was prophe-
sied by the youthful "Crimson" editor, "the torch lives
on . . . as indestructible as philosophy itself."

Works of Whitehead

Lucien Price describes Whitehead's life as a
"three-volumed one"; Volume I, Cambridge University;
Volume II, London; Volume III, Cambridge, Massachu-
setts.(4) Whitehead himself told Price that "he had
a sense of having lived three lives in three successive
epochs; the first from 1861-1914; the second during the
war of 1914-1918; and the third, after the first world
war."(5) His critics and commentators also commonly
group Whitehead's works into three periods almost

identical with the above divisions. The first period
embraces his mathematical career from 1891-1913. The
second or transition period marks Whitehead's works in
the philosophy of natural science and extends roughly
from 1914-1923. The third or metaphysical period
corresponds to Whitehead's fruitful years at Harvard
from 1924-1947.

Mathematical Period (1891-1913)

Whitehead's first book, A Treatise on Universal Algebra,(6) published in 1898 was an attempt to
unite into one single work by means of symbolic logic
many individual strands. Whitehead admits that he was
influenced by Hermann Grassman's Ausdehnungslehre
(1844) and Ausdehnungslehre (1862), Sir William Rowan
Hamilton's Quarternions (1853), and George Boole's
Symbolic Logic (1859).(7) The Treatise not only gives
us occasional glimpses of Whitehead's philosophy of
mathematics at the time, but it also was responsible for
his being elected to the Royal Society in 1903. When
the work was reviewed by Hugh MacColl, an esteemed
logician, Whitehead was judged to "have accomplished with
rare ability" the task he had set for himself. But
MacColl hastened to add that he was judging the whole work
from his knowledge of only one-fifth of the contents.
The work, like Grassmann's before it, was never fully
understood nor appreciated by mathematicians or logicians.
The aim of unification of concepts, a characteristic
trait of Whitehead, is illustrated beautifully in
Universal Algebra which possesses a unity of design
which is really remarkable, considering the variety of
its themes. With this work Whitehead begins a life-long
assault on the traditional quantitative conception of
algebra. In the Preface a distinction is made between
mathematical definitions which possess an existential
import and conventional mathematical definitions lacking
the same. The former type of definition, states Whitehead, "is the result of an act of pure abstraction,"
and is the starting point of applied mathematical sciences.
As such these definitions require more than "the mere
test of self-consistency" for verification. "In order
that a mathematical science of any importance be founded
upon conventional definitions," he continues, "the entities created by them must have properties which bear
some affinity to the properties of existing things."(8)
Thus, as early as 1898, the importance of any mathematical or logical systems, for Whitehead, stems from its
interpretation as representing properties of the real
world of existents.

4

The 1898 _Treatise_ dealt mathematically with the space of geometry. In the belief that the properties and operations of this space could form a uniform method for the interpretation of the various algebras, a generalized conception of space was the prominent ideal of the work.

Shortly after the appearance of _Universal Algebra_, Whitehead collaborated with his pupil Bertrand Russell on the monumental three-volumed work, _Principia Mathematica_ (1910-1913) which attempted to make pure mathematics an extension of a systematized deductive logic. This work represents the greatest advance in the field of logic since Aristotle. While it was in progress, the great revolution in physics occurred impressing upon Whitehead the fact that even our best generalizations are subject to qualifications unknown to us, and that the most that can be expected is a continuing approximation to truth. Victor Lowe comments that Whitehead had planned but never completed a fourth volume on geometry which would have incorporated the work of Minkowski, Einstein, and the growth of logic after 1910.(9)

During the time he was working on the _Principia Mathematica_ Whitehead published a small but important treatise, "On Mathematical Concepts of the Material World," also commonly called the "Memoir of 1905".(10) The classical concept of the world due to Newton; namely that the ultimate world entities are the trio of space, time, and matter is mathematized by Whitehead in _Principia_ symbolism and found to be totally inadequate in the description of a dynamic world. Whitehead presents alternate mathematical world concepts which he feels better fit a changing universe. This "Memoir" and several minor mathematical treatises including "The Axioms of Descriptive Geometry" (1907), and _An Introduction to Mathematics_ (1911) are of value for their brief statements of philosophical doctrine, not intended to be such for sure, but which give an insight to the natural bent of Whitehead's thoughts during his supposed "pre-philosophical" period.

The mathematician Whitehead appears, then, as a geometrician attempting to develop a _unified_ science of space, a first-rate logician pioneering in the _unification_ of the entire field of mathematics within the field of logic, and a critic of the Newtonian foundation of physics on the grounds that it did not meet the demands of either modern science or the experience of a dynamic universe.

5

He asserted that mathematics should be <u>applicable to</u>
<u>existing reality</u> and not be a merely formal system. His
interest in physics and his passion for the principle of
economy led him to introduce monistic, mathematical concepts of the world, the ultimate entities of which were
vector-like lines of force.

The influence of Bertrand Russell's philosophy
is quite apparent in Whitehead's works of this period.
Russell's major philosophical contribution at this time
was <u>The Philosophy of Leibniz</u> which fascinated Whitehead
to such an extent that his later description of "actual
entities" bears no small resemblance to the Leibnizian
doctrine of monads. As Whitehead enters the second
state of his intellectual career in 1914, one of his
major preoccupations is a typical Russellian problem--
how the exact world of science is related to the "rough"
world of everyday experience.

<u>Philosophy of Science Period</u> (1914-1923)

The second period of Whitehead's works is called
the "Philosophy of Natural Science Period" and extends
roughly from 1914-1923. It is during this time-span that
Whitehead made the transition from mathematician to philosopher. Epistemological problems are pondered and a
theory of perception emerges alongside Whitehead's con-
tributions to the philosophy of science. It is this
period of Whitehead's works with which our study is
mainly concerned. According to Lowe the initial motive
to this phase of Whitehead's work was to provide a <u>logical</u>
<u>analysis</u> <u>of</u> <u>space</u> for the <u>Principia</u>.(11) This led White-
head to an <u>epistemological</u> criticism of the classical
concept of <u>the material</u> world and the elaboration of a new
concept founded on his own type of empiricism.

Minor treatises appeared in the early years of
this period. In April, 1914, Whitehead addressed the
First Congress of Mathematical Philosophy at Paris.(12)
The address was entitled "La Theorie Relationniste de
l'Espace", and it marks the adoption of the relational
theory of space by Whitehead.

Three of Whitehead's papers, his first purely
philosophical essays, appeared in 1915, 1916, and 1917.(13)
The first, "Space, Time, and Relativity", was read to the
Aristotelian Society and published in their 1915-1916
<u>Proceedings</u>. The relation of sense perception to scien-

tific concepts, especially space and time, constitutes
the theme of this essay. The task of deductive science
is seen as the <u>construction</u> <u>of</u> <u>the</u> <u>concepts</u> <u>applying</u> <u>to</u>
<u>the</u> <u>data</u> <u>of</u> <u>sense</u> <u>perception</u>, a task which dominates
Whitehead's intellectual activities during this period
of his career.

"The Organisation of Thought", the second
essay of the trilogy (not to be confused with a later
book of essays of the same name) is a main source of
Whitehead's empirical beliefs. The third, "The Anatomy
of Some Scientific Ideas", was by far the most important
of these minor transitional works since it provides a
detailed account of Whitehead's early view of perception. Insofar as these essays supply not only an
analysis of perception but also its relation to science,
they can be thought of as a completion of the "Memoir
of 1905" which neglected both these problems.

The major works of this natural philosophy
period are the three volumes: <u>An Enquiry Concerning</u>
<u>the Principles of Natural Knowledge</u>,(13) <u>The Concept</u>
<u>of Nature</u>,(15) and <u>The Principle of Relativity</u>.(16)
These three (commonly referred to as the "1920 books")
share the same topic--Whitehead's foundations for a
philosophy of natural science based on perception but
meeting the needs of modern science. Whitehead's
answer to the problem of providing the scientist with
a coherent set of meanings based on relations manifested in experience to replace the Newtonian trinity
of space, time, and matter was the method of extensive
abstraction, the summit of these three works. <u>The</u>
<u>Concept of Nature</u> is a less technical, more readable
work than its predecessor; whereas the last of the
trilogy, <u>The Principle of Relativity</u>, is quite technical
in its approach and contains the deduction of a general
theory of relativity.

Smaller works appeared during this time which
indicate Whitehead's continuing interest in education.
Four addresses concern the problem of space, time, and
perception. "Uniformity and Contingency" (1922) was
Whitehead's presidential address to the Aristotelian
Society. "Time, Space, and Material: Are They, and If
So in What Sense, the Ultimate Data of Science?" was
the title of a symposium with Lodge, Nicholson, Head,
Mrs. Stephen, and H. Wildon Carr in 1919. Another
discussion entitled "The Idealistic Interpretation of

Einstein's Theory" took place in 1922. In 1924, Carr, Sampson and Whitehead took part in a symposium on "The Problem of Simultaneity: Is There a Paradox in the Principle of Relativity in Regard to the Relation of Time Measured to Time Lived?"

Thus, during the philosophy of science era, we see that what began as a mathematical critique of Newton's world view developed into an epistemological criticism which necessitated Whitehead's formulation of a theory of perception. He was not interested in the mere mathematics of the relational theory of space and time; he searched for the correspondence which he felt must exist between the refined scientific elements employed by the physicists and the observable natural entities known in human perception. As a philosopher of science Whitehead develops the mathematics of this correspondence in his method of extensive abstraction. The "why" of the correspondence he relegates to the realm of metaphysics. This question together with the ontological status of the entities of the method will be tackled during his Harvard years.

Metaphysical Period (1924-1947)

The last period of Whitehead's works, his metaphysical period, extends from about 1924-1947. Now most likely encouraged by the work of Samuel Alexander, Whitehead turns his attention to the exposition and formulation of an all-inclusive speculative philosophy which would synthesize his preceeding work in the philosophy of nature with a coherent philosophy of organism.(17) Personal dissatisfaction with several crucial parts of the 1920 books spurred Whitehead on. During this period he published many works on a variety of subjects, including religion, art, and history. Religion in the Making was published in 1926; The Aims of Education and Other Essays and The Function of Reason, in 1929. Science and the Modern World (1925)(18) and his masterwork, Process and Reality (1929)(19) provide certain revisions, refinements, and shifts of emphasis in Whitehead's epistemology, metaphysics, and method of extensive abstraction. Symbolism, Its Meaning and Effects (1927)(20) contains Whitehead's mature epistemology which is an attempt to answer Hume. Adventures of Ideas (1933) was Whitehead's last full-length book. During his last years at Harvard only several minor works were printed.

This was the climax of an intellectual career which spanned fifty years. Whitehead's thoughts had expanded from the mathematical to the epistemological and had finally reached the metaphysical heights. His dissatisfaction with the static Newtonian world concept led him to a philosophy of process, a coherent cosmology which attempted to fit the facts of relativity physics. He began as a mathematician and ended with a cosmology whose mathematical scheme meant that no entity might exist independent of the others. Lowe comments on Whitehead's brilliant but diversified career:

> His first object was a great intellectual synthesis, universal algebra. He went on to another, and another, always one at a time--but in his conversations and reflections he was constantly touching on all the conditions involved in human existence. If it be also true that mathematics and metaphysics are naturally akin, then it is impossible to imagine a set of conditions (world conditions of the late nineteenth and early twentieth centuries) more favorable to the creation of a philosophy.

> The man fitted the conditions perfectly. The philosophy of organism is the ultimate intellectual achievement of the nineteenth century. The centuries to come will profit far more than we.(21)

Whitehead's Theory of Space and Time

Summary of Method of Extensive Abstraction

What began as a mathematico-logical criticism of the Classical Concepts of the Material World in the "Memoir of 1905" soon developed into an original philosophy of science, the fundamental aim of which was a reconstruction of the bases of mathematics and science in accord with sense perception. Gradually Whitehead developed theories of space and time in light of the theories of twentieth-century science and the evidence of common sense experience. At the occasion of his death, the notice in Philosophy and Phenomonological Research read: In the philosophy of science, Whitehead's major contribution consists of "The Principle of Exten-

9

sive Abstraction".(22) This Method is Whitehead's conceptual instrument for defining the apparently simple concepts of space and time such as "point", "line", and "instant" in terms of relations given in sense perception.

The formulation of the Method began in the 1905 "Memoir", and though the bulk of its exposition is in the 1920 books, it is not until the final refinements are made in Process and Reality that its growth is completed. Since the Method is grounded in the immediate data of experience, a knowledge of Whitehead's early theory of the perception of events is absolutely essential to any attempt to evaluate it. Thus, an analysis of Whitehead's epistemology will be undertaken in Chapter III as a prolegomena to our critique of the Method. If it can be shown that: (1) perception for Whitehead does endow natural entities with definiteness, and that (2) by a study of model theory, the Method is indeed a mathematical model, then much of the criticism charged against the Method will prove meaningless. Most criticisms seem to center around two main points: (1) the fact that events have exact demarcations instead of vague boundaries, and (2) sense experience does not warrant the conclusion that the field of extension is dense. In order to grasp the weight of these charges it will be useful for our purpose to include here an elementary, concise account of Whitehead's method of extensive abstraction as well as some representative views about its value.

During the time of his mathematical work in collaboration with Bertrand Russell on the Principia Mathematica, Whitehead experienced a desire to elaborate a formal logical system that would embrace all the forms of relatedness manifested in the world. It was his belief that the scientific concepts of space and time are based upon relationships which are disclosed in the perception of nature. Thus, Whitehead wanted to bridge the gulf between the world of sense perception and the world of science by applying the logic of relations to the world of sensed space and sensed time. By so doing, he hoped to define the abstractions of science in terms of spatial and temporal events which are the actual objects of perception. His efforts in this respect resulted in the method of extensive abstraction of which Bertrand Russell writes:

10

I have been made aware of the importance of this problem (the relation between the crude data of sense and the space, time, and matter of mathematical physics) by my friend and collaborator Dr. Whitehead . . . I owe to him the definition of points, the suggestion for the treatment of instants and "things", and the whole conception of the world of physics as a <u>construction</u> rather than an <u>inference</u>. What <u>is</u> said on these topics here <u>is</u>, in fact, a rough preliminary account of the more precise results which he is giving in the fourth volume of our <u>Principia Mathematica</u> (never published).(23)

In our preliminary account of the method of extensive abstraction we will restrict ourselves to Whitehead's derivation of the points of space. One respect in which the space of sensed experience differs from the space of geometry and physics is in regard to points. No one has ever touched or seen a point. Therefore, the points of science must be abstractions or logical constructions from some complex grouping of sense objects. Though points are commonly thought of as simple and infinitely small, these characteristics are not strictly required by geometry. All that geometry demands is that points should have mutual relations possessing certain properties. It is quite possible that an assembly of sense data would exhibit such relations.

Whitehead observes that there are no infinitely small sense data; anything we see has some finite extent. The world is made up of events possessing volume and duration. An event at first appears as an undivided whole, but under scrutiny it can be mentally divided into parts contained within the whole. Thus events may be contained within another like a set of Chinese boxes. One event overlaps or <u>encloses</u> other events. This relation of enclosure is used to define a point as a certain <u>class</u> of spatial objects which would be said to "contain the point". Whitehead proceeds as follows: if we begin with any set of volumes or surfaces, they will not ordinarily converge to a point. But, by using the "principle of convergence to simplicity with diminution of extent" (a key principle developed as early as the 1915-17 essays), the volumes get smaller and smaller. Of any two volumes, however, one always must enclose another, that is to say,

there is no smallest member of the set of volumes.
Then we begin to have conditions enabling us to treat
the set as having a point for its limit. Certain
hypotheses concerning the relation of enclosure are required for this, but we shall omit a discussion of them
now for the sake of simplicity. A point is finally
defined as the class of objects which enclose members
of an enclosure series which possesses a punctual type
of convergence. The route of convergence is called by
Whitehead an abstractive set of events. An example of
an abstractive set would be the set of spheres concentric
to a certain point. Each abstractive class is composed
of an infinite series of successively smaller events converging towards, but never reaching, a terminal event.
By simplifying and extending certain relations in this
process, Whitehead eventually arrives at the ideal simplicity of "nature at an instant", and goes on to derive
physical laws of relativity and universal gravitation.

Debates Among Critics

Since Whitehead's major contribution to the
field of philosophy of science is the principle of extensive abstraction, his merit rests on its success in
achieving its goal which was to reconstruct the bases of
mathematics and science in accordance with sense perception. Judgments on the success and validity of the
method differ. Because several of Whitehead's critics
offer similar arguments we will state several representative views which will encompass all the major attacks
upon the Method. Three major opponents of the Method are
V. F. Lenzen, Adolf Grünbaum, and Ernest Nagel. Since
each of these has been responded to by at least one of
Whitehead's defenders, we will analyze three major
"debates": the Lenzen-Murphy Debate, the Grünbaum-Mays
Debate, and the Nagel-Lowe Debate.

Lenzen-Murphy Debate

V. F. Lenzen in "Scientific Ideas and Experience"(24) claims that Whitehead fails in his attempt to
derive the fundamental concepts of mathematical physics
from the immediate data of experience since he is inconsistent in his use of the term "ultimate fact". In some
contexts Whitehead means by this term a fundamental
concept, whereas in other contexts he means fundamental
data. These need not be the same. Lenzen endeavors to
show that Whitehead's "durations" employed in the
definition of a moment (instantaneous nature) are not

12

immediately given to sense-awareness since a duration
is ascribed both unlimited spatial and temporal extent.

> In the first place a duration is
> defined to be an event of infinite spatial
> extent. But an entity of infinite dimen-
> sions is never an immediate deliverance of
> sense-awareness. Such an entity can be
> known only by means of a conceptual
> construction. . . In the second edition
> of the Principles Mr. Whitehead ascribes
> unlimited temporal extent to a duration.
> This revision further deprives a duration
> of the character of an immediate deliv-
> erance of sense-awareness.(25)

Though we will discuss durations in detail in
Chapter III of this paper, it should be noted here
that the above passage is a misreading of Whitehead who
defines durations as being unbounded spatially but
bounded temporally. Lenzen's reference to the second
edition of the Principles is obviously to Note IV in
which Whitehead discusses the significance of an event
backwards and forwards throughout an entire time-
system. Whitehead admits the possibility of temporally
infinite events but these are not called "durations".

Lenzen goes on to criticize the idea of an
abstractive class of durations. The durations below the
threshold of awareness are constructs of thought and, as
such, cannot be apprehended in sense-awareness.

To summarize Lenzen's arguments so far: the
derivation of a moment from the immediate data of perception in the method of extensive abstraction fails
because Whitehead postulates: (1) elements which have
infinite extent, (2) elements which have a temporal
thickness less than the threshold value, (3) an infinite set of elements, and (4) elements with a
definiteness not given in sense-awareness. The same
conclusion holds for the derivations of points, lines,
surfaces, and other mathematical entities.

Lenzen then attacks Whitehead's derivation
of instantaneous nature from empirical data in which
Whitehead uses an abstractive set of limited events to
which he corresponds a series of quantitative expressions. The series of events "s" has no last term, but
the series of quantitative expressions "q(s)", though
not possessing a last term, does converge to a definite

13

limit. Lenzen denies that any quantitative series made up of empirical measure numbers which are of essence inexact can ever approach an exact limit. Therefore, the concept of nature at an instant is derivable only from ideal constructions.

Murphy in "Ideas and Nature" first addresses himself to these arguments of Lenzen: (1) that the continuity of events containing no least and no greatest parts is not given in sense experience, and (2) that no given elements have the exactitude necessary for the required convergence to a limit.

As for the first argument, Murphy agrees with Lenzen, but qualifiedly adds that the <u>character</u> of extension is given as infinite. That is, we perceive events as extended, and this property demands that there be no extent that is not part of a larger extent and none which does not contain extended parts. If this be granted as flowing from the homogeneity of the whole-part relation applied to extension, then the infinity required for convergence will be a genuine fact about the experienced events. In other words, the infinity of events is not immediately given in perception, nor is it a property of our awareness. It is, however, a <u>character</u> of that of which we are immediately aware, and thus is a fact about the world given in sense awareness. This is all Whitehead meant, according to Murphy.

In refutation of the second argument of Lenzen concerning the convergence of a quantitative series corresponding to a series of events, Murphy answers similarly. The convergence is not asserted of the measurements but of the <u>quantities</u> measured and these two are not identical. If they were, why would we speak of a "margin of error" between the measurement and the measured? If the two are distinct and the approximation is due to the inaccuracies of measurements not to the measured quantity, there is no reason to deny such quantities to events.

Murphy claims that Lenzen is guilty of a double assumption. Lenzen first assumes that the required properties of events must belong to sense data by a two-termed relation. For example, continuity is a character of events. According to Lenzen either the sense datum is given as continuous or it is not continuous at all. Or in the case of measurement, either a quantity is a measurement or it is a constructed ideal. But, according to Whitehead, both continuity and

14

measurement are relations between the given events.
Thus, Murphy's response to Lenzen's charges that the
events of sense awareness and the events to which the
postulates of extension apply have different characters
is that they are the same events but with different
characters in the two contexts. A description of events
is a relational affair not found in immediate data as a
simple quality but a relation of the events characterized by the data.

Grünbaum-Mays Debate

Adolf Grünbaum, renowned author, philosopher,
and scientist severely attacks Whitehead's method of
extensive abstraction in an article published in the
British Journal for Philosophy of Science (Vol. IV).
Starting from C. D. Broad's account,(26) Grünbaum claims
that Whitehead's attempt failed as indeed do all such
positivistic constructive attempts to exhibit geometrical
notions as derivative from sense data. He gives five
arguments. The first states that the Method is vitiated
by Zeno's mathematical paradox of plurality because of
a violation of two conditions stated by Broad which
points must satisfy: (1) points must have to each other
the kinds of relations which geometry demands, and
(2) points must be related to finite areas and volumes
so that the volumes can be exhaustively analyzed into
sets of points. The Zeno paradox referred to is that
since spatial and temporal intervals are extended, it is
self-contradictory to regard them as aggregates of unextended points and instants. Georg Cantor's point-set
theory rests precisely on this conception. The only way
it can be consistently claimed that an interval is an
aggregate of denumerable points of zero measure is if
the aggregate is super-denumerably infinite.(27) Whitehead then must discover in sensed nature a super-
denumerable infinity of abstractive sets to define
points. Naturally any such attempt will fail since
sense awareness cannot exhibit the actual existence of
such a collection in sensed nature.

Secondly, Grünbaum argues that the convergence
of the Method's abstractive classes is fatally ambiguous
and that the modifications in Process and Reality do not
remove this crucial ambiguity. The Dedekind-Russell
definition of irrationals(28) provides decisively for a
clear differentiation between every two irrationals
however close they are in magnitude. Consider two
distinct points $x=0$ and $x=10^{-1000}$ which are separated

from each other by a continuum of points. Sense perception provides no means for distinguishing the abstractive classes required by Whitehead to confer a separate identity upon such points. Thus, says Grünbaum, "the Method obliterates the very precision of meaning made possible in the statement of physical laws by the employment of real variables".

Whitehead, in response to critical suggestions by T. de Laguna, modified his theory of abstractive classes in Process and Reality where he no longer requires the members of abstractive regions to be sensed; a new relation of non-tangential inclusion is defined as characteristic of an abstractive class. Grünbaum holds as his third argument that this revision still does not remove his charge of the ambiguity of convergence.

The fourth objection of Grünbaum is a most common one, i.e., that abstractive classes do not belong to the domain of sense-awareness because they contain an infinite number of regions. Whitehead, according to Grünbaum, simply claims the continuity of inclusion among the members of abstractive sets as the guarantee of the existence of the infinite series of subsensory terms. Since Grünbaum feels that this argument from the continuity of inclusion is a tacit appeal to the infinite divisibility of physical space-time and not sensed space-time, he rejects it.

Lastly, Grünbaum dismisses Ushenko's defense of Whitehead's principle.(29) Ushenko claims that the infinite number of regions is permissible not because it is observable but because it is a legitimate concept of formal mathematics. Each region does not have to be exhibited; it is sufficient that any region should, in principle, be observable.(30) Ushenko feels that Whitehead's definition of point is a conceptual or logical construction and, as such, needs illustration not exemplification in order to be empirically justified. Grünbaum objects to this interpretation claiming with Broad that Whitehead's physical theory makes existential assertions about point-events, mass-points, and, therefore, requires exemplification. Ushenko's stronger condition, according to Grünbaum, is "a futile logical possibility of observation entirely devoid of the required existential import". Likewise his weaker condition fails.

To summarize Grünbaum's positions: the principle of extensive abstraction fails because: (1) it

16

requires the notion of a non-denumerable infinity of
perceivables which is untenable, (2) it obliterates the
precision of meaning made possible in the statement of
physical laws by the use of real variables and (3) its
own epistemological assumptions render gratuitous, if not
meaningless, the postulate of the continuity of inclusion
among the members of abstractive sets.

Wolfe Mays in Chapter VII of his book, The
Philosophy of Whitehead, responds to Grünbaum's criticism
which, Mays points out, relies heavily on the acceptance
of Broad's interpretation of the Method as based on sensationalist foundations. Mays is of the opinion that
such an interpretation is not a true one though he admits
that "Whitehead does not always make it sufficiently
clear whether his method is to be taken as an algorithm
or as an exact description of some actual process of
convergence". Mays cites Bertrand Russell's opinion that
Whitehead was examining the problem of defining the tra-
ditionally primitive geometric entities in terms of
empirical data from the point of view of mathematical
logic.(31) Mays is inclined to believe that Whitehead's
principle is an abstract model, a piece of applied logic
"enabling us to get from volumes to points". Whitehead
was using a mathematical model, to make clear certain
relations appearing in perception. Such an interpretation
would harmonize the "Memoir of 1905", the Method as found
in the 1920 books, and as revised in Process and Reality
where it reappears as a purely formal logical investigation.

Mays responds to Grünbaum's charge of ambiguity
of convergence by defending Whitehead on the ground that
we can encounter the inexhaustibility of an abstractive
set in thought. Though Whitehead does assume the ideal
infinite divisibility of space, he does so in order to
save geometry. Grünbaum assumes in his criticism that
perceptual space or the structure of appearance is
isomorphic with the real number continuum. Whitehead
is partly to blame for this since he appears to assume
that his Method could arrive at the serial order among
moments in a time system which has the Cantor-Dedekind
type of continuity.(32) This does seem difficult if not
impossible. Grünbaum further assumes that physical space
and time necessarily have the continuity of the real
number line whose elements are non-denumerable. Mays
points out that Whitehead himself said we had no way of
judging whether any physical quantity has the continuity

17

has the continuity of the series of real numbers though he later assumes such because of mathematical simplicity not for experimental reasons nor a priori assumptions.(33) Mays comments:

> Whitehead's conception of a continuum as a connected system of regions rather than a series of discrete points brings him closer to the intuitionist's continuum, where the fundamental relation is that of part to whole rather than element to set.(34)

Mays answers Grünbaum's charge of the circularity of Whitehead's definition of volume by pointing out that the volumes are simple indivisible elements and do not presuppose points. If the Method is a technique for translating a series of convergent volumes into points, the circularity charge is not important since this is a characteristic of any axiomatic system. Mays holds with Ushenko that the postulate of continuity of inclusion as well as the notion of an infinite series is adopted with the rest of modern mathematics.

To summarize May's position: he admits that Whitehead is not always consistent but the inconsistencies are not as great as Grünbaum claims. The interpretation which Mays feels is best attuned to Whitehead's general position is that Whitehead was not trying to construct a geometry from sense experience, but rather using a mathematical model to make clear certain relations appearing in perception.

Nagel-Lowe Debate

Ernest Nagel in Chapter Nine of his book, Sovereign Reason, charges that the principle of extensive abstraction fails insofar as it does none of the things that can be expected from an instrument devised for a criticism of abstraction. In fact, says Nagel, it is a "mathematical calculus whose application to the matters at hand raises the very problems it was intended to solve." Again we meet the charge that no empirically given subject matter involves infinite sets of volumes which Whitehead uses to define a point. In addition, no experiment could decide whether an alleged point is indeed a point if as a precondition the experimenter would have to understand the relations between an infinite set of objects. Whitehead's principle, concludes Nagel, does not explain how any of

18

the concepts of science defined by infinite series or
limiting processes are either connected with or applied
to finite subject matter.

Victor Lowe, in an excellent chapter of his
book, Understanding Whitehead, discusses in detail the
method of extensive abstraction. He addresses himself
to the charges rendered by several critics of the Method
including Ernest Nagel. Lowe feels that if Whitehead
intended to offer his Method as an instrument for the
criticism of abstraction, it is odd that he should have
christened it "the method of extensive abstraction".
Whitehead's purpose was not to criticize abstraction as
Nagel mistakenly believes, but to "replace the unclear
idea of an extensionless point by a systematically
stated abstraction from spatial experience". Lowe agrees
that infinite sets of volumes are not given in sense perception if we interpret this to mean the possibility of
actually discriminating these volumes by observation or
experiment. However, Lowe holds that empirically given
spatiality seems to involve more. As to Nagel's second
charge, Lowe asks what kind of "something" could ever be
subjected to experiment to see if it is a true point or
an imposter? Because chalk dots can be so observed, we
know they are not points.

Lowe believes Whitehead's method is not merely
a formal mathematical system. Somehow, it does have
concrete meaning. He feels that we must start with
observed entities and relations in order to define any
theoretical concept, but then we must interpolate and
extrapolate. Whitehead's applications are, in Lowe's
judgment, "empirically well-based constructions of
ideal concepts".

Summary of Debates

Whitehead's method of extensive abstraction has
been judged a failure by Lenzen, Grünbaum, and Nagel. The
reasons given for this failure are varied. Many of the
charges involve either the relation of perception and the
perceived world to mathematical entities or the techniques
employed by Whitehead. The invalidity of the use of
mathematical infinity--obviously unperceived--recurs again
and again. Lenzen charges that durations of unlimited
extent are not given in sense-awareness. Almost all of
Grünbaum's arguments involve, in one way or another, the
misuse of infinity on Whitehead's part--an infinity which

19

is not observable. The same can be said of Nagel's
charge that no empirically given subject matter involves
infinite sets of volumes. Murphy, Mays, and Lowe attempt
to answer these charges. Murphy believes that though the
infinity of events is not given in perception, this infinity is a character--a fact--of that given in perception.
Mays defends Whitehead's use of infinity by suggesting
that such a use is valid in a mathematical model--a piece
of applied logic--which is the status of the method. Lowe
also believes that the method is a mathematical construction, but that it is more than that; it has empirical
meaning. Thus, the core of the debate seems to center
around two main points: (1) the correspondence between
perceived entities and mathematical entities; the former
supposedly inexact and vague, the latter, exact and
definite, and (2) the validity (or invalidity) of the
use of mathematical concepts such as infinity, convergence,
etc. in an instrument which is to derive scientific entities from observable entities.

A Mathematical Model

        It will be the aim of this paper to examine
further the suggestions offered by Mays and Lowe; that
is, that the method is a mathematical construct or model,
but is at the same time empirically based. The paper
will attempt to confirm these viewpoints by the three
following steps. First, the Method will be traced from
its origins in the "Memoir of 1905" and "La Theorie
Relationniste de l'Espace" through the refinements and
revisions made in Process and Reality. Since most of
Whitehead's critics have not examined thoroughly the
earlier works of 1905 and 1914, it is hoped that by
analyzing them in detail a clearer understanding of the
Method as a mathematical construct will be accomplished.
If the Method is a mathematical model in the contemporary
sense of the term it must fulfill certain requirements.
The fundamental requirement of such a model is that it
must possess the property of isomorphism. An isomorphism
displays similarity of structure between the two fields
of comparison by setting up a one-to-one correspondence
between the entities and relations of both fields. If it
can be shown that perceived natural entities possess
exactness and definiteness, then the correspondence
between these perceived entities and the mathematical
entities of the method of extensive abstraction is easily
demonstrated. The Method is then accurately judged a

"mathematical model." However, it must be shown that perception for Whitehead does _indeed_ endow the fragmentary sense data with this definiteness and exactness. For this purpose, the second task of this paper will be a study of Whitehead's early perceptual theory up to 1924.

However, even if a critic demands that in order for the Method to be true to Whitehead's wishes, the isomorphism must be set up between the mathematical entities of the Method and the natural entities _per se_ (and not the natural entities as perceived), it can still be shown that the Method remains a mathematical model because it fulfills several functions of models. This will involve an appeal to contemporary literature on the philosophy of the scientific model--the third and final step of this paper.

In recapitulation: to resolve the debates currently raging among scholars, this dissertation will show that, indeed, the method of extensive abstraction from its very origin in 1905 through its final, metaphysical appearance in _Process and Reality_ is a mathematical model. This will be achieved by (1) tracing the evolution of the Method from the "Memoir of 1905" through the three 1920 books, briefly noting the modifications made in _Process and Reality_, (2) analyzing Whitehead's early theory of events and their perception, and (3) presenting several expert contemporary views on the philosophy and function of the scientific model. Such a study will clarify the status of the method of extensive abstraction as a mathematical model. As such its worth in the philosophy of science will be recognized as an invaluable contribution in bridging the gap between the level of theoretical science and the level of sense observation.

NOTES

1. Lucien Price, Dialogues of <u>Alfred North White-</u><u>head</u> (New York: Mentor Books).

2. "Autobiographical Notes," <u>The Philosophy of</u> <u>Alfred North Whitehead</u>, ed. Paul A. Schilpp ("Library of Living Philosophers"; Evanston and Chicago: Northwestern University, 1941), p.7. Hereafter this volume will be referred to by the editor's surname only.

3. As quoted by William Ernest Hocking in the excellent biographical paper, "Whitehead as I Knew Him," <u>Journal of Philosophy</u>. Our reference is from the reprint found in <u>Alfred North Whitehead, Essays</u> <u>on His Philosophy</u>, ed. George Kline (Englewood Cliffs, N.J.: Prentice-Hall Inc., 1963), p. 16. This latter volume will hereafter be referred to by the editor's surname.

4. Price, p. 9

5. <u>Ibid</u>.

6. Alfred North Whitehead, <u>A Treatise on Universal</u> <u>Algebra, with Applications</u>. (Hafner Publishing Company, New York, 1960). Further references to the book will be designated as UA.

7. Whitehead, "Autobiographical Notes," Schilpp. p. 9.

8. UA, p. vii. (Italics mine.)

9. Victor Lowe, <u>Understanding Whitehead</u> (Baltimore: The Johns Hopkins Press, 1962) pp. 11 and 177. Hereafter this book will be referred to as Lowe, UW.

10. This memoir will hereafter be referred to as MC. It is reprinted in <u>Alfred North Whitehead: An</u> <u>Anthology</u>, eds. F.S.C. Northrop and Mason W. Gross (New York: The Macmillan Company, 1953). References

to MC will be from this anthology which is easily
accessible to the public. The Anthology will be
referred to as N&G.

11. Lowe, UW, p. 177.

12. Publication was delayed two years. The work
finally appeared in Revue de Metaphysique et de Morale,
Vol. XXIII, May, 1916, pp. 423-454. My own translation of pertinant passages of this rather long, technical
address appears in the Appendix of this work. This paper
will be referred to as RTS.

13. All three were published as the concluding
chapters of The Organisation of Thought (London:
Williams and Norgate, 1917). The first two also appear
in The Interpretation of Science: Selected Essays by
Alfred North Whitehead, ed. A. H. Johnson ("The Library
of Liberal Arts," Number 117; Indianapolis: The Bobbs-
Merrill Company, Inc., 1961), hereafter referred to as
IS. All three were reprinted with slight omissions in
1929 as Chapters X, VIII, and IX respectively of The
Aims of Education and Other Essays (New York: Macmillan Company, 1929). Our quotations will be from
the 1967 Free Press Paperback Edition of this work,
called hereafter AE.

14. Cambridge: Cambridge University Press, 1955:
it will be called PNK.

15. Cambridge: Cambridge University Press, 1955:
it will be referred to as CN.

16. Cambridge: Cambridge University Press, 1922.
This work, hereafter referred to as PRel, has long been
out of print. The main part of the Preface and the
first four chapters, however, which comprise the non-
mathematical part of the work, are reprinted in N&G.

17. For an analysis of the influence of Samuel
Alexander upon Whitehead, see A. H. Johnson, Whitehead's
Theory of Reality (New York: Dover Publications, Inc.,
1962). Also, see Lowe, UW, pp. 264-66.

18. Lowell Institute Lectures; New York: The
Macmillan Company, 1931. Hereafter, this volume will
be called SMW.

19. New York: The Macmillan Company, 1929. This
book is currently available in a paperback reprint by
Harper & Brothers, New York, 1960. It contains the
same pagination as the original edition. Because
all these editions abound in errors, one should consult
"Corrigenda for Process and Reality," in Alfred North
Whitehead, Essays on His Philosophy, ed. George Kline
(Englewood Cliffs, N. J.: Prentice-Hall Inc., 1963)
pp. 200-207. Process and Reality will be referred to
as PR, and Kline's book will be referred to by the
editor's surname.

20. Barbour-Page Lectures: New York: The Macmillan
Company, 1927. Hereafter, the work will be called Sym.

21. Lowe, UW: pp. 294-95.

22. As quoted by Lowe, UW, p. 61

23. Bertrand Russell, Our Knowledge of the External
World (New York: Mentor Books by arrangement with
George Allen & Unwin Ltd., 1960), pp. v-vi.

24. V. F. Lenzen, "Scientific Ideas and Experience,"
University of California Publications--Philosophy Vol.
VIII (1926), pp. 175-189.

25. Ibid., p. 183. (Italics mine.)

26. C. D. Broad, Scientific Thought (London:
Routledge & Kegan Paul LTD, 1923), pp. 38-52. Lowe
states that this account by Broad is seriously misleading by suggesting that Whitehead began with the
colored patches we see, the lumps we touch etc., crude
things given to sense awareness but quite unlike the
exact concepts of geometry. Whitehead then, by gather-
ing these into classes and filling them out, arrived
eventually at complex entities which have the logical
properties of points. This, says Lowe, is a serious
but common misreading of Whitehead. Extensively related
events, not the sensa which we perceive as qualifying
some of them, are the terms with which the Method
operates. Lowe, UW, p. 79.

27. A denumerable set is one that can put into a
one-to-one correspondence with the natural numbers.
Aleph zero is the cardinal number of the denumerable

sets. Super-denumerable sets cannot be put into one-to-one correspondence with the set of natural numbers. Ex. set of irrationals, set of real numbers.

28. See Chapter IV for an explanation of the Dedekind "cut."

29. A. P. Ushenko, "Einstein's Influences on Philosophy" in Albert Einstein: Philosopher-Scientist, ed. Paul A. Schilpp ("The Library of Living Philosophers", (Evanston and Chicago: Northwestern University, 1949), pp. 632-645.

30. This is Ushenko's stronger criterion. He gives a weaker one by which all that is required is an illustration of the kind of thing (point) that the definition is about.

31. Bertrand Russell, Preface to J. Nicod's Foundations of Geometry and Induction, trans. P. P. Wiener (London: Routledge & Kegan Paul LTD., 1930), p. 7. Nicod himself thinks that Whitehead's principle can be taken as a construction of geometry rather than as an analysis of the real world; his whole account applying only to mathematical volumes for which, unlike points, a specific interpretation does exist in sense perception if we begin with a sufficiently large volume. See pp. 40-43.

32. PNK, p. 115.

33. A. N. Whitehead, Essays in Science and Philosophy (New York: Philosophical Library, 1947), p. 203. Hereafter referred to as ESP.

34. Mays, pp. 115-116. The Intuitionist school in the philosophy of mathematics is Kantian in their concept of number. They reject the Law of the Excluded Middle and any mathematical proofs that require an infinity of steps. Their most renowned leader is Brouwer. Intuitionists regard the continuum problem as meaningless. For a concise account of their philosophy see: Max Black, The Nature of Mathematics (London: Routledge & Kegan Paul, 1933), pp. 186-210.

CHAPTER II

CONCEPTS OF THE MATERIAL WORLD

Mathematical Concepts of the Material World

In order to understand adequately the mature cosmology of Process and Reality, it is necessary to have acquaintance with two earlier works of Alfred North Whitehead which are primarily mathematical and logical in character: namely, the Memoir of 1905, "On Mathematical Concepts of the Material World," and the paper "La Theorie Relationniste de l'Espace." Without this essential study, the revisions and refinements made in Process and Reality would appear disjunctive with Whitehead's philosophy of nature which emphasized the epistemological rather than the formally mathematical. If we are to judge knowingly of the status of the method of extensive abstraction we cannot limit the evidence to the epistemological era of Whitehead's works. Only with a knowledge of the very beginnings of the Method will we be in a position to defend Whitehead against his critics, most of whom pay little or no attention to his first works on the problem of space and time.(1)

Whitehead states his goal in writing the "Memoir of 1905" in the Preface where he writes:

> The object of this memoir is to initiate the mathematical investigation of various possible ways of conceiving the nature of the material world. In so far as its results are worked out in precise mathematical detail, the memoir is concerned with the possible relations to space of the ultimate entities which (in ordinary language) constitute the 'stuff' in space (particles of matter).(2)

Thus, Whitehead wishes to show how one could

110447

construct in a rigorous, axiomatic manner alternative concepts of the physical world. This is a unique attempt in so far as he is applying for the first time symbolic logic to concrete subject matter.

A "concept" of the material world is a world-picture, a diagramatic or schematic model of physical nature. The "classical concept" of the material world is the model drawn by Newton who used three different entities; namely, positions of space, instants of time, and particles of matter. In the 1905 Memoir, Whitehead translates Newton's classical concept into mathematical-logical language and criticizes it on two points. First and foremost, Newton's world picture with its three primitive terms of spatial points, instants of time, and material particles violates the Principle of Economy (Occam's Razor) which pleads for fewer terms and fewer relations between the terms. Secondly, the mathematized Classical Concept does not account for change and motion of material particles unless we add to it an indefinite (perhaps infinite) number of extraneous mathematical relations--one to account for each change in position for each moving particle. Obviously, the number of relations required in this procedure represents another gross violation of Occam's Razor. Therefore, Whitehead develops several alternative mathematical world concepts which require fewer primitive terms and fewer extraneous relations. Wolfe Mays suggests that Whitehead under-took this work to reduce the number of basic concepts physics starts from. The advances which physics has made demand changes in the different kinds of extraneous relations in terms of which the physical laws are stated. The essential relations from which geometry is derived, however, need not be changed. Whitehead could admit that the basic elements assumed in physics--space, time, and matter--have remained the same. However it is his contention that the kind of matter postulated and the law matter follows may have changed as physics has progressed.

Though the "Memoir" is primarily a mathematical investigation, Whitehead himself says that it has an indirect bearing on philosophy since it disentagles the essentials of the idea of a material world from the accidents of one particular concept. He is not yet interested in the philosophical problems of how the subject perceives the world nor the existence of his possible models of the material world which are purely speculative endeavors.

Whitehead sets forth fundamental definitions
which at first may seem rather strange to an uninitiated
reader. The material world is conceived as a "set of
relations and of entities which occur as forming the
'fields' of these relations." Great emphasis is placed
on these very important relations. Whitehead proceeds
to define the fundamental relations of the material
world as "those relations in it which are not defined in
terms of other entities, but merely particularized by
hypotheses that they satisfy certain propositions. The
hypotheses and also the propositions which the fundamental
relations satisfy are called the Axioms of the world concept. These ingredients then--the complete set of axioms,
definitions, and the resulting propositions--constitute a
material world concept.

The complete class of entities which are members
of the fields of the fundamental relations is called the
class of "ultimate existents." No concern is given to
the philosophic question of the existence of the material
world so conceived. Whitehead concurred with Russell in
the belief that time must be composed of instants, and he,
therefore, included instants of time among the ultimate
existents of every world model. However, though instants
are included in the category of ultimate existents, they
are excluded from the class of "objective reals." This
rather strange distinction supplies us with a clue to
Whitehead's thinking about the ontological status of such
instants--instants of time exist; yet they are not objective realities:

The class of ultimate existents, exclusive
of the instants of time, will be called
the class of Objective Reals.

Critique of the Classical Concept

Whitehead now considers five concepts of the
material world. What is characteristic of the Newtonian
Classical Concept is that its ultimate existents are three
mutually exclusive classes of entities; points of space,
particles of matter, and instants of time. The simple
elements of space are points, and geometry studies the
relations between them. Matter, the ultimate "stuff"

29

that occupies space consists of entities called particles
which are associated with the points by relations which
are expressed by saying that a particle "occupies" or is
"at" a point. Occupation, then, is a triadic relation
holding between a particle of matter, a point of space,
and an instant of time.

Opposed to Newton's world concept is Leibniz's
theory of the relativity of space. An absolutist theory
of space and time claims that perceived spatio-temporal
events occur in moments of time and in positions of space.
These time moments and spatial positions are posited by
the absolutist as independent realities. The moments of
time form a homogeneous one-dimensional medium called
"absolute time." Likewise, the spatial points form a
three-dimensional homogeneous medium called "absolute
space." A relativistic theory of space like that pro-
posed by Leibniz claims with the absolutists that spatio-
temporal events are, indeed, the perceived entities.
However, they do not occur in soace and in time. On the
contrary, moments of time and spatial positions are
derived relations which exist among the perceived events.
For an absolutist, moments of time and points of space
are assumed a priori; for a relativist they are derived a
posteriori.

Though Whitehead had not yet adopted the relative theory he comments that Leibniz's view means that
the points of space as conceived in the classical concept
are not to be taken among the objective reals. Whitehead's
main concern at this time, however, is not to uphold or
combat any specific theory of the material world, classical
or Leibnizian, but to exhibit various concepts. He was
setting up the possibilities--most likely to examine the
benefits and defects of the various mathematical models
exhibited in order to choose the one most to his standards.
His main criterion for judging the value of each model
would be Occam's Razor. Secondarily, he was interested
in formulating concepts "not inconsistent with some, if
not all, of the limited number of propositions at present
believed to be true concerning our sense perceptions.
This is a most revealing statement since it indicates that
as far back as 1905, Whitehead was not merely concerned
with a logical endeavor but was striving to ground his
mathematical models on somewhat of an existential base.

Dualistic concepts

Whitehead distinguishes two general types of world concepts. Concepts which demand two classes of objective reals (points of space and particles of matter) are called the "dualistic concepts"; those demanding only one such class, "monistic concepts." Newton's classical concept with points and particles forming the class of objective reals (instants of time are excluded from this class) is thus dualistic, while Leibnizian concepts, in general, are monistic. Occam's Principle of Economy asserts an instinctive preference for a monistic and not a dualistic world concept.

Besides the class of objective reals, the fundamental relations between entities are of major importance in every world concept. The essential relation, denoted by R, is a single finite polyadic relation of linear order by means of which the various geometrical entities are defined. The "field" of the essential relation will vary according to the various concepts.

The time relation, also of importance in every concept, is a dyadic serial relation (denoted by T) having for its field only the instants of time(3) At the time of the writing of the "Memoir," Whitehead did not espouse a relational theory of time. On the contrary, space and time are regarded as independent of each other, and no thought is given to the derivation of time from something more basic. Instants of time, as we have noted, are posited as ultimate existents in every one of the five world concepts formulated in the "Memoir."

Every world concept, in addition to the essential relation (which provides for the derivation of geometry) and the time relation, requires "extraneous relations" which relate matter to the points of space and instants of time(4) In order to determine the positions of particles of matter it may be the case that these extraneous relations be indefinite or even infinite in number.

Whitehead now outlines his method for developing a concept of the material world. Four logical stages of progress are delineated: (1) definition of those entities capable of definition in terms of the fundamental relations,(5) (2) deduction of those properties of the defined entities which do not depend upon the axioms, (3) selection of the group of axioms which determines the concept, and (4)

31

deduction of propositions which involve among their
hypotheses some or all of the axioms of the third stage.

It may be somewhat disconcerting that Whitehead
places the selection of the axioms only in the third
stage. However, he points out that psychologically the
order of these stages tends to be inverted. We first
choose propositions of the second and fourth stages and
then those of the first and third stages. Those chosen
in the second and fourth stages are not picked arbitrarily
but because of their "parallelism with the propositions of
sense-perception." Psychologically we begin with what is
given to the senses; logically, we do not. The logic
cares for the mental concept, but it is the data given in
sense-perception that guarantees that the constructed
concept is indeed a model of the material world. To put
it simply, when we attempt to put geometry on a formal
basis, we begin with our ordinary experience which makes
us intuitively aware of the properties of geometrical
figures. We then try to derive these intuitively experienced properties from more basic propositions.

Whitehead's chief concern in the "Memoir of 1905"
is the selection of the definitions and axioms of the
system. Only in future works will he devote his energies
to the problems inherent in choosing propositions in
"parallelism with the propositions of sense-perception."

The order of procedure is now clear. A certain
relation R (the essential relation) which holds between a
certain definite number of entities is considered. The
class of entities between which this relation holds is
called the "field" of R. Definitions of entities allied
to R and to the field-entities are then given. These
definitions involve no hypotheses as to the properties
of the essential relation, but are, of course, of no importance unless the essential relation does indeed have
some certain properties. Otherwise they would be trifling.
The axioms (hypotheses as to the properties of the essential
relation) are then given. Finally such deductions are given
as are necessary to elucidate the concept.

Punctual concepts

Those concepts of the material world in which the
class of objective reals is composed of spatial points or
material particles or both, Whitehead calls the punctual
concepts. The first such considered is the Newtonian

32

Classical Concept. Because its class of objective
reals is subdivided into points of space and particles
of matter, the Classical Concept is dualistic as well
as punctual. Following Veblen's axiomatic system which
bases Euclidean geometry on one class of undefined
entities--points--and one undefined serial relation
between points, Whitehead mathematizes the Classical
Concept. The triadic essential relation he uses
establishes the linear order of the points "a", "b,"
and "c." This relation is not symmetrical: "a" and "b"
cannot be interchanged.(6)

        After the essential relation has been posited,
definitions of segments, straight lines, figures, linear
figures, triangles, and planes are given. These, Whitehead
says, are sufficient to exhibit the dependence of the
various geometrical entities on the essential relation
allowing us to pass on to the selection of the axioms.(7)
Note should be made of the fact that none of the definitions
contain any reference to length, distance, area, or volume.
The reason for this is that none of these ideas appear in
the axioms, and only such definitions are given as are
necessary for the enunciation of the axioms. These ideas
can be introduced by definition at any later time by the
well-known projective methods. With the enumeration of the
twelve axioms which are needed as hypotheses in the propositions of the fourth stage, the whole of geometry can be
deduced.(8)

        Though the resulting deductive system is a product
of beauty, Whitehead regretfully comments on the lack of
correspondence between the concept and the world of change
which we experience. Since the instants of time were not
originally included in the field of the essential relation,
there is as yet no contact between the time relation and
the essential relation. All we have so far is an essential
relation ordering spatial points linearly and definitions
of geometric entities. This is a far cry from the living,
experienced, mobile world. Whitehead comments:

        Nothing could be more beautiful than the above
        issue of the classical concept, if only we
        limit ourselves to the consideration of an
        unchanging world of space. Unfortunately,
        it is a changing world to which the complete
        concept must apply.(7)

To remedy this defect, a class of particles is posited where
the particles are the ultimate entities composing the

fundamental "stuff" which moves in space. The assumption
of this class of material particles as fundamental objective reals renders the Newtonian Concept dualistic.
These particles form part of the field of a class of
extraneous relations. Each such extraneous relation is
conceived as a triadic relation, which in any particular
instance holds between a particle, a point in space, and
an instant of time. Since the field of each extraneous
relation possesses only one particle, the Classical Concept
has to admit a class of as many extraneous relations as
there are members of the class of particles. These relations
provide for the definitions of velocity and acceleration in
terms of which the laws of dynamics are defined.

Thus, the major defects Whitehead criticizes in
the Classical Concept are two. First, three independent
classes of entities are employed; namely, points of space,
instants of time, and particles of matter. Since it is
possible to reduce this number (by making matter a mode of
relating space and time, for instance) the Classical Concept violates Occam's Razor. Secondly, an indefinite or
infinite number of extraneous relations is required to provide for motion. No worthy deductive axiomatic system
would be characterized by so many extraneous relations.

As an attempt to remedy the first defect of a
superfluous number of primitive entities, Whitehead constructs
two monistic variants of the Classical Concept. In Concept
II (which we will call Russell's Concept since it was
suggested by Bertrand Russell) (10) material particles in space
are abolished, and the extraneous relations are transformed
into dyadic relations between points of space and instants
of time. A material particle, exiled from the realm of
objective reals, now becomes a mode of relating a point of
space to an instant of time. This is no great loss for
Whitehead since he feels that matter was introduced in the
first place only to give the senses something to perceive.
If a relation can be perceived, Russell's Concept has every
advantage over the Classical Concept since the results are
the same. But as to the question as to whether a relation
(and therefore, the material world) can be perceived, Whitehead dismisses the problem as a philosophical one with which
he has no concern.

The second monistic variant of the Classical
Concept (Concept III of the "Memoir") will be referred to in
this paper as the Leibnizian Concept. Since the points are
assumed to be in motion, their relations to each other
differ at different instants. How then does one account for

34

the permanence of matter? To answer this problem Whitehead has to have recourse to the axiom of persistence.
This axiom is unnecessary for the geometrical reasoning
of the Concept but is an integral part of the physical
side of the model. In the comparison of the states of
the objective reals at different instants, the reals
assume the character of particles. Thus, the persistence
of matter is explained by motion alone.

Only one extraneous relation is necessary to
show how different points can have the same position at
different instants. This one extraneous relation enables
a definition of both velocity and acceleration. The
Leibnizian Concept has advantages over both Newton's
Concept and Russell's Concept since it reduces the class
of extraneous relations to one member. But there is
absolutely nothing to distinguish one part of the objective reals from another part except differences of
motion. Matter is moving particles. Motion is of the
essence of matter.

Whitehead's Linear Concepts

The real innovation of the "Memoir of 1905"
lies in Whitehead's two linear concepts (Concepts IV
and V) which depart widely from the Newtonian Classical
Concept. The objective reals--at least those which
together with the instants of time form the field of
the essential relation--have properties normally associated with straight lines considered throughout their
whole extent as single indivisible entities. Points are
classes of these simple linear entities and are no
longer primitive entities. Whitehead specifies these
linear objective reals as the modern physicists' lines
of force which he takes to be the ultimate unanalysable
entities which compose the material universe. Though
lines of force suggest ends, the linear objective reals
have no such properties analogous to these ends.(11)

Whitehead's first linear concept (Concept IV)
has two alternative forms, one dualistic and the other
monistic. In both concepts points are derivative and
not posited as basic entities. Motion is defined in
terms of only one extraneous relation determining the
kinetic axes by reference to which all motion is
measured. The derived complex points do not persist
but disintegrate from instant to instant. A material
corpuscle is a volume made up of points. These

35

corpuscles of matter have moving through them linear
reals which make up the ether lying between the material
volumes. Since there is, in one sense, something--not
mere space--between two distinct corpuscles; namely, the
objective linear reals possessed in common, the ancient
controversy concerning action at a distance becomes
irrelevant. Whitehead does state, however, that in a
sense there is a direct action between two distinct
corpuscles.(12) Both alternative forms of Whitehead's
first linear concept require an indefinitely large class
of extraneous relations.

As we have already noted, points are no longer
primitive, ultimate entities. They are defined complex
entities--certain classes of linear objective reals.
This idea is not new to mathematicians since in projective geometry the projective point is a class of straight
lines converging to the ideal point at infinity. The
obvious difficulty of these linear concepts is the circularity inherent in the definition "a point is to be
defined as the class of objective reals concurrent at a
point." To overcome this obstacle Whitehead develops
two separate answers, The Theory of Interpoints and The
Theory of Dimensions--direct forerunners of the method
of extensive abstraction.

Theory of Interpoints

The Theory of Intersection-points (shortened
into "Interpoints") is one way Whitehead attempts to
remove the circularity inherent in the definition of a
point as being the class of linear objective reals
concurrent at a point. In speaking of the projective
point as a bundle of lines assuming the descriptive
point (the ordinary point of geometry) Whitehead poses
the problem of defining the projective point without
such an assumption. In so doing he makes another assumption; namely, that all points (descriptive, projective,
etc.) are complex in character and not primitive elements.
He thus actually abolishes the ordinary descriptive point
by regarding it as derivable from linear reals more fundamental than geometric points and lines.

Whitehead's first and second linear concepts
(Concepts IV and V of the Memoir) require the Theory of
Interpoints. In the first linear concept, the interpoints are the only points; there are no others. In the
second linear concept, the interpoints are only portions

36

of points, that is parts of the bundle of lines which
constitute points. A point may contain no interpoints
or many. The axioms of both linear concepts are two
alternative sets of hypotheses as to the properties of
the essential relation in connection with which the
Theory of Interpoints assumes importance. Some axioms
are identical in both concepts. These Whitehead states
in his Theory and derives their consequences.

In the Theory of Interpoints points are constructed from linear entities by means of the notion
of "similarity of position" in a pentadic essential
relation. The definition of similarity of position is
as follows:

An entity, "y," will be said to have a
position in the pentadic relation R,
similar to that of the entity, "x," with
"a" as first term and "t" as last (fifth)
term, if, whenever the relation holds
between five terms, "a" being the first
term and "t" the last term, and either "x"
or "y" or both occurring among the other
terms, the relation also holds when "x" is
substituted for "y" (whenever "y" occurs),
and also holds when "y" is substituted for
"x" (whenever "x" occurs).(13)

As long as the linear order is preserved, "x," "y," and
"z" may be substituted for each other. Spatial position
is the possibility of a class of entities occupying the
same position.

The essential relation in the Theory of Interpoints and in both Whitehead's linear concepts is a
pentadic one: the linear objective real "a" intersects
the linear objective reals "b," "c," "d" in the order
bcd at the instant "t." The instant of time, the temporal
entity, is here included with the essential relation.
This notion of intersection in order of three linear
objective reals by a fourth at an instant of time is a
fundamental relation between the five entities.

Using both the notions of intersection and
similarity of position, Whitehead defines an interpoint
as the total class formed by the linear real "a" and the
class of linear reals "x," "y," "z" having a similarity
of position which "a" intersects. He then defines a

class of interpoints having an interpoint order at a
time "t." Starting from this relation of order.
Euclidean geometry can be constructed in a manner
similar to that of the Classical Concept. However,
there are some differences. The geometrical points
are now complex and refer to instants of time, and
punctual lines and planes are now series of interpoints
and have a time reference.(14)

The Theory of Dimensions

      In preparing both for his second linear con-
cept in which he will construct a three-dimensional
geometry and as a separate answer to the problem of
circularity, Whitehead develops the Theory of Dimensions. The theory is relevant to any definite property
which is a property of classes only and is only a
property of some classes. In the second linear concept,
the relevant property is one defined by certain axioms
and termed "homaloty." In an Elucidatory Note the
property of flatness is defined, and in the Theory of
Dimensions, this property of flatness is denoted by
"ϕ." With this assumption, three is the ϕ-dimension
number of the space. Since the property of flatness
deals with the straightness of lines not based on
measurement, it plays an important part in establishing
the equality of spaces. ϕ-points of not less than three
dimensions are defined on the lines of ideal projective
points. A point now becomes simply that class of
straight lines concurrent at a point. Whitehead comments
that the analogy with Klein's ideal or projective points
is obvious. "Only when the present theory is applied,
it will be found that the original 'descriptive' point
has entirely vanished." From such a class of straight
lines (a point), Whitehead proceeds to define other flat
geometrical elements and is able to ccnstruct a three-
dimensional geometry necessary for his second linear
concept (Concept V). By using further axioms, Whitehead
could construct the whole theory of projective geometry
apart from order and the distinction of harmonic conju-
gates.

Whitehead's second linear concept--Concept V

      The monistic second linear concept is the most
important part of the "Memoir of 1905." The essential
relation is a pentadic one with only one extraneous

relation required for the measurement of velocity and
acceleration.(15)

There are seventeen axioms for this concept
as opposed to twelve in Newton's world concept. However, a larger field is covered and in a monistic concept
there often is an increase in the number of axioms and
derived theorems corresponding to the decrease in undefined entities.

Whitehead uses both the Theory of Interpoints
and the Theory of Dimensions to define points, and the
points at infinity are called "cogredient points." The
concept of "cogredience" appears later in Principles of
Natural Knowledge where it is the relation between an
event here present and its associated duration. In the
"Memoir of 1905," however, cogredience deals with a
parallelism between linear objective reals which have
the same geometrical order. An Axiom of Persistence
and an Axiom of Continuity are needed, and though all the
axioms are axioms of geometry, Whitehead states that the
geometry in the second linear concept includes more than
does geometry in the Classical Concept of Newton, because
it considers the relation of the linear objective reals
and interpoints to the points, punctual lines, and
punctual planes. Thus, Whitehead claims that the
geometry of Concept V merges into physics more than does
the geometry of the Classical Concept.

Whitehead describes alternative possibilities
of the development of his second linear concept which
are of interest to us only because Whitehead feels that
he has formulated a mathematical concept of the material
world which fits reality better than the Classical Concept. No attention was given to the detailed "how" of
the correspondence between his mathematical world model
and the world it models, but nevertheless, it is quite
clear that the author did not intend the "Memoir" to be
a purely speculative mathematical treatise. Though the
world concept came first in the order of the mind, it was
Whitehead's concern "to exhibit concepts not inconsistent
with some, if not all, of the limited number of propositions at present believed to be true concerning our
sense-perceptions." In model theory, a theory is a
linguistic entity consisting of a set of sentences.
Models, on the other hand, are non-linguistic entities
in which the theory is satisfied.(16) If we admit the
set of propositions concerning the material world to
form the theory T, then all five of Whitehead's mathemati-

39

cal world concepts are models of T--imperfect to be
sure, but models nevertheless.

The closing paragraph of the "Memoir" indicates
that Whitehead was dissatisfied with his models:

> The complete Concept (Concept V) involves the
> assumption of only one class of entities as
> forming the universe. Properties of 'space'
> and the physical phenomena 'in space' become
> simply the properties of this single class of
> entities. . . the ideal to be aimed at would
> be to deduce some or all of them from more
> general axioms which would embrace the laws
> of physics. Thus these laws should not pre-
> suppose geometry but create it.(17)

It was this dissatisfaction that led Whitehead to a more
profound study of space, time, and perception culminating
in the method of extensive abstraction.

Comments

In Whitehead's two linear world concepts
(Concepts IV and V) the basic elements are hypothetical
linear reals from which points are derived. In projective
geometry parallel lines are conceived of as converging at
an ideal point at infinity. Such an assumed ideal point
is called the "projective point"; it is made up of an
infinite set of converging straight lines. This is the
idea Whitehead uses in his linear world concepts with
the exception that his derived points are considered as
ordinary points and not as ideal points at infinity. It
is a small step from a converging series of straight lines
to a converging series of overlapping volumes. It is the
latter concept Whitehead will employ in the method of
extensive abstraction in which "events" (spatio-temporal
volumes) are the basic entities and the whole-part enclosure relation is the essential relation. The Method
uses the principle of convergence to simplicity and
involves the assumption of a convergent series. The
change from the derivation of points from linear reals to
the derivation from a converging series of overlapping
events occurs in "La Theorie Relationniste de l'Espace."
What is interesting to note is that in Process and Reality,
the basic entities in the revised method of extensive
abstraction appear once again as purely logical existents;
they are not events.

The Relational Theory of Space

In the years between 1906 and 1914, Whitehead published several mathematical articles.(18) As late as 1909 Whitehead believed that no decisive argument for either the relational or absolute theories of space had as yet been presented. But when he addressed a congress of logicians in Paris, in April, 1914, the title alone--"La Théorie Relationniste de l'Espace"--tells us that he had now adopted the relational position. This paper is quite central to a study of the method of extensive abstraction since it marks the transition between the "Memoir of 1905" and the philosophy of nature works. It is an attempt on Whitehead's part to mathematize the relativistic theory--a task he had begun by exhibiting the Leibnizian concept in the 1905 Memoir. Several important relations are introduced which later form part of the method of extensive abstraction; namely, the "whole-to-part relation," the notion of "covering," and "occupation" of space. More important perhaps is a more sophisticated derivation of points from primitive overlapping volumes.

It must be remembered that Whitehead was at this time preparing the fourth volume of the *Principia Mathematica* which was to be a logical treatment of the subject of geometry. Whitehead had often complained that philosophers worked with a wholly inadequate two-termed logical apparatus. He therefore aimed to reformulate the concept of space in the light of the new symbolic logic of polyadic relations. Unfortunately, the intended volume was never completed. However, the logical treatment of space developed in the 1914 address represents Whitehead's research and thought done in preparation for the never-to-be-completed geometric volume of the *Principia*.

Different Meanings of the Word "Space"

"The Relational Theory" begins with a distinction of four different meanings of the word "space." The primary distinction is between apparent or perceptive space and physical space. Apparent space is the place of objects insofar as they are perceived by us; physical space, the space of a hypothetical world, is the space of science.

Apparent space is a function of the perceiver, and as such, is different for each individual. The

41

apparent space of "A" consists of certain relations between the things which appear to "A." Naturally, these relations differ from the relations between things which "B" perceives. Apparent space is further subdivided by Whitehead in an attempt to unify all the individual apparent spaces of men into a totality. For this purpose he distinguishes immediate apparent space which is the space which appears now to an individual perceiver from complete apparent space which is the sum total of everyone's immediate apparent space. This totality, called "complete apparent space" is the idea, a mental construct (obtained by mentally adding the apparent immediate space of "A" with that of "B" and so on) of the totality of the world complete with apparent objects. Complete apparent space no longer refers exclusively to the perceiving subject. It is the space of the perceived world, the ordinary space referred to by men in conversation, and it supposes a kind of conception of the physical world since no one perceiver can experience immediately--here and now--the totality of the physical world.

The third meaning of "space" is physical space, the space of science which is the same for all. Whitehead states that the relations between the objects of physical space correspond exactly to the relations between our sensations. That which appears immediately to the perceiver are apparent objects which are related to a complex of relations among physical objects. As to the nature of the correspondence or the parallelism between these relations, Whitehead is not yet ready to give us any assistance. However, he does admit that it is a fundamental scientific problem, one which is habitually presented as a causation of sensations by the states of the physical world. All that he is willing to say is that the only essential characteristic of this physical world of science is the parallelism of its events to the perceptions of the knowing subjects. The physical world of science is a logical hypothetical construction. All progress in the analysis of this physical world is made by replacing the unstable objects of apparent space by the more permanent objects of physical space such as molecules, atoms, and electrons.

The fourth use of the word "space" is abstract space, and the science corresponding to it is abstract geometry. Whitehead does little else than mention this mathematical space, indicating once again his unconcern with mathematical systems which have little or no existential import.

42

Thus, the four meanings of "space" are:
immediate apparent space, here and now uniquely preceived
by a subject; complete apparent space, the logical construct of the totality of immediate apparent spaces;
physical space, the space of science which is the same
for all; and abstract space, the mathematical space of
geometry.

Mathematical Model for the Relational Theory of Space

Contrary to traditional geometry which has as its
primitive elements, points, lines, surfaces, and volumes,
the relational theory of space for both apparent and
physical space demands more primitive entities. Points
must be complex entities, logical functions of relations
between objects, if we are to avoid points having an
absolute position. Thus, Whitehead adopts as his primary
task the definition of points as the function of relations
between objects. First, there is a world of things in
relationship with each other. Then there is space whose
primitive entities are defined by means of these relations
and whose properties are deduced from the nature of these
relations. In the relational theory of space, physical
objects should not be thought of as first existing in
space and then acting one upon the other. On the contrary,
physical objects are in space because they act one upon the
other. Space is "nothing else than the expression of certain properties of their interaction." (19)

Whitehead begins his treatment of the relational
theory by stating that the concept of a world existing in
space is that of a "Class of relations s." A world
founded on such a class is called an "s-world"; the
entities forming the field of such a class is called the
"class of s-objects." All this is quite reminiscent of
the constructions found in the "Memoir" with one important
difference--the new exposition can be interpreted either
perceptually (apparent space) or physically (physical
space).

The essential relation (denoted by R) of the
s-class is any relation such that "xRy" signified "x
has the relation R to y." Whitehead uses Principia
symbolism throughout, but again, his verbal translations
and explanations are sufficient for us to gain an understanding of his thoughts. In the complete apparent world,
if "s" represents the class of relations between a possible
perceiving subject and the apparent (perceived and extended)

object, "pRx" means that the possible perceiving subject "p" perceives the apparent, extended object "x" following the sensible mode "R." In the physical world, if "s" is the class of direct relations between physical objects, "xRy" means that the physical object "x" has the direct relation "R" to the physical object "y."

The geometrical concept of a point for the s-world is then defined. In order to do this, Whitehead first defines a relation "E_s" (inclusion-s) which is analogous in its formal properties to the relation of "whole-to-part." "Point" has different meanings in apparent space and physical space. In the perceived apparent space, a point is an "area or a volume sufficiently small so that the subject is incapable of introducing in it an exact division into parts." Such minima sensibilia lack neither surface nor volume--only the stability necessary for division. In physical space, a point is an area or volume sufficiently small such that a division is useless in the actual state of science. Both these interpretations, however, are approximative usages of the concept of a geometric point as one which has essentially and exactly neither parts nor extension. It is this very possibility of an approximative interpretation of exact theorems which Whitehead asserts is necessary for an exact science to be of any value.

This is Whitehead's aim for geometry--not to define simply and logically "points," "lines," and "surfaces," but to supply definitions which keep the general and simple properties which are attributed to them in geometry, and which permit us to substitute for them approximative concepts (of points, for example) in the approximative propositions of simpler domains of thought where the fundamental concepts appear.

Whole-to-part relation

In the apparent world extended objects are perceived as unities and not as collections of points. Objects are given in perception as a unique whole--their points are not separately perceived. If, however, attention is fixed on one or several of the parts, the immediate perception of the spatial whole is lost. Whitehead says that then the whole must be mentally reconstructed as the logical whole of the perceived parts. Therefore, an object of great dimensions which can never be perceived as a unique whole ever remains as a mental construction, the

44

<u>whole</u> of its perceived parts.

In the <u>physical world</u> convenience dictates that
each s-object must be conceived as an ultimate unity. By
means of a defined relation Whitehead assigns to these
objects the logical properties which we assign to the
whole and part. The relation he calls "E_s" (inclusion-s),
a relation defined and derived by certain members of the
s-class. Once defined this relation can then be used to
define points. The relation of inclusion is reflexive,
transitive and asymetric.(20) Whitehead assumes several
hypotheses as properties of this inclusion relation, one
of which is the hypothesis of infinite divisibility which
is the foundation of the continuity of space. Whitehead
admits that the proof is not evident; indeed, in apparent
space, the existence of <u>minima visibilia</u> seems to contradict it. In physical space this hypothesis is adopted for
convenience since it makes mathematical deductions possible.

Since the relation of whole-to-part forms an
essential part of the Method it is worth our time to make
several comments at this point. Whitehead is certainly
aware of the difference between the approximative use of
a point as a "sufficiently small volume" and the exact
geometric concept of point. Yet the value of any mathematical system is to supply exact definitions which are
true to the mathematical properties, but which at the same
time allow us to <u>substitute</u> an approximative concept.
He is cognizant of the fact that infinitely divisible
volumes are <u>not given in perception</u>, but merely <u>adopts</u>
the infinite divisibility hypothesis for mathematical
<u>convenience and simplicity</u>. There is no reason to believe
that in the development of the Method, he ever changed his
opinion on the status of this hypothesis.

Fundamental spatial concepts

With the aid of the inclusion relation Whitehead
proceeds to the definition of fundamental spatial concepts.
(21) Whitehead's method consists in first defining geometrical entities such as points, lines, and surfaces in
such a manner as to obtain "material T-points," "material
T-lines," and "material T-surfaces." These latter correspond to the occupied points, lines and surfaces. If we
accept the hypothesis that every position is occupied by
an s-object, then the definitions are complete. But if
we admit an unoccupied space, that is a space unoccupied
by s-objects, then Whitehead would have to construct a
generalized theory of ideal points.(22) These ideal points

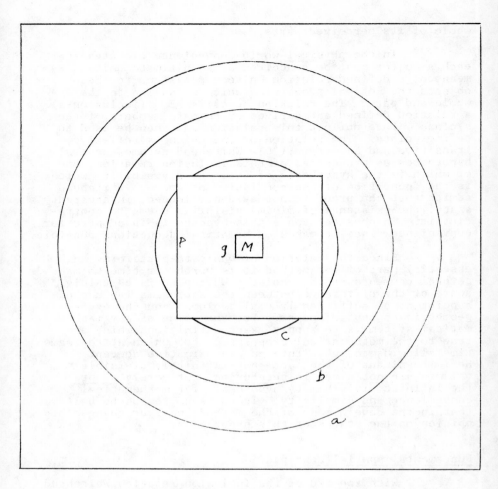

Fig. 1--The geometric inclusion serial class is formed by the series of concentric circles, a, b, c . . . with center M which is not an apparent indivisible element. The class of concentric squares p, q, ... has the same center M. The two classes are inclusion-equal. (23)

are the points of the complete space of geometry. An
ideal point is said to be occupied when there is a
material T-point which corresponds to it; otherwise, it
is unoccupied.

The general conception which Whitehead now has
to state precisely is that of an object progressively
cut into smaller and smaller parts until its dimensions
have disappeared, and there remains only one point. This
"point" or "conceptual limit" is obtained by means of
s-objects and the inclusion relation and the principle
of convergence. Whitehead admits that the meaning of
convergence of an infinite series of numbers is precise
and definite, but, since s-objects are not numbers, this
mathematical meaning of convergence does not simply apply.
He adds that outside of a special hypothesis "the ideal
of a 'conceptual limit' as it is applied to series of
s-objects still remains without precise meaning."
Therefore, critics who charge Whitehead with insisting
that perceived volumes do converge to a point, do so
rashly and no doubt have not been made aware of Whitehead's
RTS position.

Whitehead then asks us to consider what he calls
a "geometric-serial-inclusion class." An example of such
a class would be a set of concentric spheres whose only
common spatial element is the center. Points, lines, and
surfaces determined by such classes need not necessarily
be situated in the interior of one another. For example,
if we take only the halves of the cylinders of one side
only of the central plane section, the geometric series
defines a common section which is on the surface of all
the members of the series. Whitehead then differentiates
the set of geometric-serial-inclusion classes according as
the convergence is towards a point, line, or surface. A
new relation of "covering" is introduced. A serial class
"a" is said to cover a serial class "b" if every member of
"a" covers a member of "b".(24) Two serial classes "a"
and "b" are equal when each covers the other. To help
picture this concept, imagine a set of concentric circles
with center M. Also consider a set of concentric squares
with the same center M. Then the two serial classes are
"inclusion equal." These relations of covering and equality
of sets are developed later in the principle of extensive
abstraction in the discussion of abstractive sets.

In discussing various types of serial inclusion
classes and their types of convergence, the problem of
perception (in apparent space) requires Whitehead to make

47

some interesting comments:

> Apparent objects are perceived as areas,
> not necessarily as planes. The interior
> of these objects is conceived, but the
> immediate apprehension is always the
> perception of a surface object. In the
> measure in which the points are directly
> perceived it must be by the perception
> of an indivisible point area. Then if
> the relations of two surface objects are
> perceived as exactly defined by a
> geometric point, then an indivisible
> point area is perceived as the point
> which defines the relation.(25)

This is not the statement of a naive mathematician-
philosopher claiming that infinitely divisible volumes--
or even indivisible points--are perceivable except in
rare circumstances. He continues:

> But when the law of convergence
> requires in its definition a
> definite point or a definite line,
> this point or this line must be a
> perceived point or a perceived line;
> consequently, the perceived point
> must be an indivisible perceived
> point area.

Comments

> Though RTS has been judged excessively long and
technical, the following views expressed in the paper are
essential to any student of Whitehead's philosophy of
science.

1) Apparent objects given immediately to the perceiving
subject are related to a complex of relations among
physical objects in the space of science. The nature of
this relationship or correspondence is not discussed in
detail though this parallelism is the only essential
characteristic of the physical world of science. This
world is a logical, hypothetical construction. Whitehead
indicates that progress in science can only be made by
substituting more permanent scientific objects for the
unstable objects of apparent space.

48

2) Points are derived as <u>logical</u>, <u>complex</u> <u>entities</u>.
They are functions of relations between objects.

3) An exact science, to be of value, must provide for
an approximative interpretation of the exact theorems.

4) The adoption of the hypothesis of infinite divisibility which is the foundation of the continuity of
space is done for <u>mathematical</u> <u>convenience</u> in <u>physical</u>
<u>space</u>. Whitehead admits that in <u>apparent</u> <u>space</u> the
existence of <u>minima</u> <u>visibilia</u> seems to contradict this
hypothesis.

5) Whitehead admits that the mathematical principle of
convergence to a conceptual limit <u>does</u> <u>not</u> <u>apply</u> <u>simply</u>
to a series of s-objects. Precise meaning of such a
convergence of s-objects could only be had by a special
hypothesis.

6) Perceived points are indivisible perceived point areas
although a point may be directly perceived in <u>exceptional</u>
cases. A point in general is the concept of the possibility of a series of subdivisions.

          With these facts clearly delineated, the prin-
ciple of extensive abstraction will be more clearly
evaluated. Whitehead now turns his attention to the
question he has ignored since the 1905 Memoir, but which
becomes increasingly more important to his work--the relationship of sense perception to scientific knowledge.

Role of Perception in the Formation of World Concepts

          Following his initial exposition of the relational
theory of space in 1914, Whitehead devoted more of his
attention to a "long and careful scrutiny of the definitions
of points of space and instants of time" required for a
satisfactory explanation of the relational theory.(27)
For three years following his 1914 address, Whitehead was
pondering this problem and was becoming immersed in the
epistemological issues accompanying it. The three published
essays: "Space, Time, and Relativity" (1915), "The
Organisation of Thought: (1916)(28) and "The Anatomy of
Some Scientific Ideas (1917)(29) are the first evidences
of his early theory of perception. As the direct successors
of the "Memoir of 1905" and "The Relational Theory of Space"
as well as the immediate predecessors of the three volumes

constituting Whitehead's main contribution to the philosophy of natural science, these essays provide an
indispensable link in the evolution of his philosophy.
We will concern ourselves with two topics from these
works: namely, Whitehead's theory of perception, and
further developments in his theory of space.

Whitehead's Realism

Before embarking on an exposition of Whitehead's
early theory of perception, it will be helpful to in-
vestigate Whitehead's brand of realism since he has been
often labeled a "realist" of one sort or another by
historians of philosophy. In fact all of the following
"tags" have been tied around the Whiteheadian corpus by
various writers at various times: "British empiricist,"
"rational empiricist," "sensationalist," "phenomenalist,"
"neo-realist," and "critical realist." To add to the
confusion each of these labels was bestowed on the strong
testimony of textual evidence. It is not our purpose in
this paper to unravel the complexities involved in neatly
categorizing Whitehead's epistemological views.(30)
However, some knowledge of the problem will be helpful as
a background for our understanding of the development of
Whitehead's theory of knowledge.

According to Victor Lowe, the early Whitehead
accepted the characteristic starting point of British
empiricism--that the immediate objects of our mind are
the contents of our perceptions. Actually, during his
natural philosophy period, Whitehead's empiricism is very
similar to the narrow logical empiricism of the positivists
mainly because of Whitehead's positivistic desire to keep
all metaphysical questions independent from science. For
Whitehead the world was a construct--the first unconscious
act of speculative thought. The similarity between this
idea of "inferential construction" and Hume's notion of
the connected world as a product of the habits of imagination is striking. So we see that Whitehead did indeed
possess some of the traits of the British empiricists,
logical positivists, and Humeans. Yet, at the same time,
to complicate the matter, Whitehead exhibits traits
which are distinctly un-Russellian, un-positivistic, and
un-Humean. In the three transitional essays of 1915-17
there is a total absence of any skepticism; radical
skepticism never interested the common-sensed Whitehead.
For Russell, Hume, and most logical positivists, the
construction of common-sense concepts is a process of

building a public world from private experiences. But
this is not Whitehead's problem--his is to attain definiteness, logical smoothness and completeness. In "The
Aims of Education" he actually denounces the problem of
building up publicity from privacy as a pseudo-problem.
At the time of these three essays, however, he does agree
that there is a problem. While he is most assuredly not
a neo-realist as far as the perception of an objective
world is concerned, he does not attack natural realism
like Russell does. Whitehead's future move into realism,
then, will not require a radical turnabout of his
thinking.

Whitehead's development

In "La Theorie Relationniste de l'Espace"
Whitehead had adopted a critical position. The physical
world was a conception. Actually he was not espousing a
realism in 1914 so much as a sensationalistic theory of
knowledge. His desire for realism only becomes apparent
in Concept of Nature. Throughout the 1920 books his
realistic theory is intermingled with his prior sensationalistic (empirical) view. In Principles of Natural
Knowledge the phenomenalistic strain is still present but
also present is a leaning toward naive realism. Molina
states that this leaning is really "a propounding not a
species of naive realism but a sophisticated theory of
the awareness of externality." In Concept of Nature
Whitehead moves towards a less phenomenalistic theory of
nature but, notwithstanding, he develops a far more sophisticated concept of experience than it would be possible if
the realism towards which he is moving were a merely naive
one. We accept Molina's conclusion that in his attempt to
establish a realism that would circumvent the bifurcation
of nature, Whitehead fails because of his deep-rooted
sensationalistic tendencies.

The Essays of 1915-17

In the three essays of 1915-17 Whitehead manifests a strong phenomenalistic, sensationalistic strain.
In "Space, Time and Relativity" he emphasizes the relation
of logic to individual experience, a relation which cul-
minates in the creation of a common world of concepts.
Yet, he was unable to avoid completely a reference to the
notion of a common world. He rejects the views of the
neo-realists at this time. Fragmentary individual

experiences are all that we know--the sole datum of
all our speculation. Whitehead's problem is "to fit
the world to our perceptions, and not our perceptions
to the world." (31) The physical world is for him, in
some general sense of the term, a "deduced concept"
because of his empirical belief that the only exact data
of the physical world are our sensible perceptions.
Since the broken, limited experiences of the individual
is capable of sustaining a deductive superstructure,
Whitehead leaps to the conclusion that experience itself
must have a certain "uniformity of texture." The
physical world is deduced not merely by a chain of
reasoning but by a deduction through a chain of definitions which lifts thought to a higher abstract level in
which the logical ideas are more complex and the relations more universal. Whitehead states:

> In my view, the creation of the world
> is the first unconscious act of specu-
> lative thought and the first task of
> a self-conscious philosophy is to
> explain how it has been done.(32)

It seems that Whitehead's main problem is that
of the relation of experience--disorderly, fragmented,
radically untidy--to scientific concepts which are exact,
neat and trim.

In "The Anatomy of Some Scientific Ideas" we
glimpse the same phenomenalistic strain and rejection of
naive realism. Though Whitehead states that we perceive
things in space (the "rough" world), the primary elements
of the scientific or "smooth" world are not directly
perceived. The object which is directly perceived somehow
corresponds to a series of events in the physical world.
The perceived object is largely the supposition of our
imagination. To use one of Whitehead's homely examples:
when we hear a cat mewing, see its arched back, feel it
rubbing against us, we recognize not only the cat but the
fact that it was glad to see us. These many direct objects
of sense must be distinguished from the single, indirect
object of thought which is the cat. We thought a cat and
imagined its feelings, but the direct objects of sense
were the sensations of hearing, seeing, and feeling.
"Such combinations of sense-objects is an instinctive
immediate judgment in general without effort of reasoning."(33)
Since the cat is mentioned as an indirect object of thought,
Whitehead is certainly not a neo-realist at this time.
There is no doubt about this as we proceed further

Whitehead goes on to explain that a single
sense-object is a complex entity and concludes that it
is already a "phantasy of thought," since a sense-object
perceived at one time is a distinct object from a sense-
object seen at another time. Likewise, there is no such
thing as a sense-object at an instant. There must be
essentially a _duration_ which permits a steady stream of
sense-presentations. (This represents a change from the
"Memoir of 1905" when instants were ultimate entities in
every world concept. Now, Whitehead rejects instants
and begins to develop his theory of "durations.")

The problem of memory and the relation between
past, present, and future events leads Whitehead to ex-
pound his Principle of Aggregation, one of the "fundamental principles of mental construction according to
which our conception of the external world is constructed."
This Principle is an inferential construction which
establishes time-relations between elements of consciousness. The Principle of Convergence to Simplicity with
diminution of extent is another important principle for
Whitehead. It is, as he says, the "master-key by which
we confine our attention to such parts as possess mutual
relations sufficiently simple for our intellects to
consider." By means of the latter principle, we can
diminish and even neglect the perplexing effects of
change by concentrating on shorter and shorter stretches
of time, thus reducing the complexity of the sense-
presentation. Further simplicity is gained by applying
the principle to spatial relations also by means of par-
titioning this static world into parts of restricted
space-content. Finally we can partition these already
restricted parts into further parts, "characterized by
homogeneity in type of sense, and homogeneity in quality
and intensity of sense."

The sense-object, therefore, is a result of
the three above processes of restriction, and the result
of an active process of discrimination--a quest for
simplicity of relations.

The law of objective stability (the law of co-
herence of sense-objects) must also be applied in
conjunction with the principle of convergence to simplicity.
All of this may be made more clear by the use of Whitehead's
own illustration of the steps involved in our perception
of an ordinary "orange."

1) The first crude thought-object of perception: We look

at an orange for half-a-minute, handle it, smell it,
note it, note its position in the fruit basket and then
turn away. The stream of sense-objects of the orange
during that half-minute is a first crude thought-object
of perception. The coincidence of space relationship
is the essential ground for the association of sense-
objects of various types such as sight, smell, and
touch. (Diverse space relations, on the other hand,
dissociate sense-objects from aggregation into a first
crude thought-object.) To achieve the "orange" in the
ordinary sense from the orange of half-a-minute requires
the two principles of aggregation and of hypothetical
sense-presentation.

2) Conceptual thought-object of perception: By means
of the principle of aggregation, the many distinct,
first crude thought-objects of perception are conceived
as one thought-object of perception if three conditions
are present: (a) the many partial streams forming
these objects must be sufficiently analogous, (b) their
times of occurrence must be distinct, and (c) the
associated sense-objects (the fruit basket in the case
of our orange) must be sufficiently analogous. We may
keep returning every five minutes to take a peek at our
orange. By aggregation we combine all these sense-
objects of an orange into the same orange. But this is
still not sufficient. The orange, says Whitehead, is
more than that. If we say that the orange is in the
cupboard if Tom has not eaten it, our words have a definite
meaning. Though at the time of the utterance of these
words, we are not directly perceiving the orange, we
imagine it with its shape, odor, color, etc. to be in
the cupboard. The metaphysical problem concerning the
actuality of the existence in the cupboard is dismissed
by Whitehead who is "only concerned with the fact that
such imaginations exist and essentially enter into the
formation of the concepts of the thought-objects of perception which are the first data of science."(34) The
imagined orange in the cupboard is formed by the principle of hypothetical sense-presentation, the "partner"
of the principle of aggregation. Whitehead puts it
this way:

> The world of present fact is more than
> a stream of sense presentation. We
> find ourselves with emotions, volitions,
> imaginations, conceptions, and judg-
> ments. . . . Imagination is necessary to

complete the orange, namely, the
imagination of hypothetical sense-
presentations.(35)

What is essential to science is our conception of the
orange: its meaning in regard to the metaphysics of
reality is of no scientific importance, so far as
physical science is concerned.(36) The orange, completed in this manner is the thought object of perception.
Whitehead strongly reminds us that the judgments and
concepts which arise in the formation of the thought-
objects of perception are mainly instinctive and not
consciously sought for and criticized before adoption.
Though the thought-object of perception is a "device
to make plain to our reflective consciousness relations
which hold within the complete stream of sense-presentation," the applications of this device are limited.(37)
Our senses can sometimes fool us. (A stick half-
submerged in water appears to be bent.) Another
difficulty arises from the fact of change. The orange
we sensed yesterday in the fruit basket in position A
is not the very same orange we sense today in the same
position. It has ripened (or withered), become a little
sweeter (or dryer). However, be that as it may, the
chief use of the thought-object is the concept of the
orange as one thing, here and now, which later can be
recognized, there and then. It works sufficiently well
to most things for short times, and to many things for
long times, despite the fact that sense presentation as
a whole "refuses to be patient of the concept." A great
part of the difficulty is removed by applying the Principle of Convergence to Simplicity. Man has the habit
of making his thought-objects too large. The change in
thought-objects of perception can be explained as a dis-
integration into smaller parts, themselves thought-
objects of perception. We have analyzed ordinary common
daily perceptual experience. This is still insufficient
for science, so Whitehead continues with a discussion of
thought-objects of science.

Thought-objects of science

        For Whitehead, the material universe is
"largely a concept of the imagination which rests on a
slender basis of direct sense-presentation." In other
words, the world as we know it is a hypothetical
thought-object of perception, with only a "slender base"

55

grounded in direct sense-presentation. Science employs
purely hypothetical thought-objects of perception to
explain some of the stray sense-objects such as sounds
which cannot be construed as perceptions of a thought-
object of perception. Science must go still further
however, and employ what Whitehead terms "thought-objects
of science" which have shed all the qualities capable
of being perceived. They are known only as results of
"a series of events in which they are implicated and
which are represented in our conclusions by sense-
presentations." Whitehead claims that it is this technique by which sense-presentations are represented in
our thought as our perception of events in which the
thought-objects of science are implicated that is the
"fundamental means by which a bridge is formed between
the fluid vagueness of sense and the exact definition
of thought."

So, we can understand what Whitehead meant
when he said that it was never the thought-object of
science which is perceived, but a complicated series of
events in which it is implicated. "If science be right,"
says Whitehead, "nobody ever perceived a thing, but only
an event." This, of course, cannot be reconciled with
traditional philosophy which conceives the thing as
directly perceived. However, the modern scientific
concept which Whitehead expounds is claimed to have the
advantage over the traditional epistemology in that
"it is enabled to 'explain' the fluid vague outlines of
sense-presentation." The problem now is the status of
sense-presentations as fluid and vague. Whitehead no-
where proves that such is the case. He assumes that
upon reflection of our own experience, we shall find
that this is so. But, this is a large assumption on
his part, to say the least:

In the 1920 books, Whitehead expounds further
his doctrine of what he then calls "scientific objects."
At this point in Whitehead's career, his theory of perception is in its germinal stage and is vague, inconsistent at times, and incomplete. The following diagram
is a recapitulation of his theory as found in the
transitional essays of 1915-17.

1. Crude Sense-Objects
   "orange" color, spherical shape, etc.

2. Actual Thought-Objects of Perception
   one orange

3a Thought-Objects of
Science molecules,
atoms, electrons

3b Hypothetical Thought-
Objects of Perception-
"points"

4b Material Points
points which are limits
of series of enclosure
objects

5b Ideal Points

Though we haven't as yet discussed Whitehead's derivation
of points, the entire process from the crude sense-objects
to scientific objects is one of search for permanence,
uniformity, and simplicity of logical relation and not
simplicity of internal structure. Scientific-objects are
characterized by permanence and uniformity. Now, let us
continue with Whitehead's discussion of "points."

Space and time

Much of what was said concerning the whole-to-
part relationship in "La Théorie Relationniste de l'Espace"
is reported in the three transitional essays in less
technical, more popular terms. Naturally, some development and clarifications can be seen. The promise made in
1914 to complete a theory of unoccupied points is fulfilled, but the context now is chiefly a discussion on
perception since a sense-object is a part of the complete
stream of presentation. Since a sense-object can also be
a part of another sense-object (temporally or spatially),
the whole-and-part relation can be applied. Whitehead
comments:

It seems probable that both these concepts
of time-part and space-part are fundamental: that is, are concepts expressing
relations which are directly presented
to us, and are not concepts about
concepts.(38)

57

        The whole-to-part relation is first and fore-
most one that holds between the sense-objects of
perception extended temporally and spatially. Only
secondarily, through the laws of convergence to simplicity, is it ascribed to the thought-objects of
perception of which they are components. Insofar as
this relation refers to directly presented sense-
objects, Whitehead writes:

        Call two sense-objects "separated" if
        there is no third sense-object which
        is a part of both of them. Then an
        object A is composed of the two objects
        B and C, if (1) B and C are both parts
        of A, (2) B and C are separated, and
        (3) there is no part of A which is
        separated both from B and from C. In
        such a case the class "a" which is com-
        composed of the two objects B and C
        is often substituted in thought for
        the sense-object A. But this process
        presupposes the fundamental relation
        'whole-and-part.' Conversely the
        objects B and C may be actual sense-
        objects, but the sense-object A which
        corresponds to the class "a" may remain
        hypothetical. . . . It is possible,
        however, that some mode of conceiving
        the whole-and-part relation between extended
        objects as the all-and-some relation
        of logical classes can be found.
        But in this case the extended objects
        as here conceived cannot be the true
        sense-objects which are present to
        consciousness.(39)

        Thus, in his genesis of points of time and of
space, Whitehead dismisses the whole-and-part relation
which holds between sense-objects in sense-time and
sense-space because, except in rare instances, these
are not sufficiently exact to lead to the logical idea
of a point. Instead, Whitehead proceeds to logicize
the whole-and-part relationship between spatially extended objects. The logical relation corresponding to
the relation of whole-and-part is that of "enclosure."
The property of enclosure, symbolized by "a E b" is
defined as "b is a part of a" or "a encloses b."

58

The field of E is the set of things (called "enclosure objects") which either enclose other objects or are enclosed by other members of the field.(40) The whole-and-part relation of sense-space is now the logical relation of "enclosure" which is transitive and asymmetrical. An enclosure object cannot be part of itself, and the principle of the indefinite divisibility of extended objects is posited. Whitehead then considers a set of enclosure objects which satisfy the three further conditions: (1) of any two of its members one encloses the other, (2) there is no member which is enclosed by all the others, and (3) there is no enclosure-object not a member of the set which is enclosed by every member of the set. He calls such a set a "convergent set of enclosure-objects."(41) Passing along the converging series from the larger to the smaller members, we eventually converge towards an ideal simplicity to any desired degree of approximation by means of the application of the principle of convergence to simplicity.

The use of the principle of convergence, however, does not yield the same type of simplicity for every route, as we have seen previously in the 1914 essay. Since time is one-dimensional, we have no difficulty with a convergent set of temporal enclosure-objects considered as a route of approximations. Such a set of temporal objects always leads to the ideal simplicity of a unique instant of time. For space, however, different types of simplicity arises. Convergence may be to a plane, line segment, or point. It is the latter type of convergence which is of interest to Whitehead who now must "tighten up" the logical property of enclosure by means of restrictions so designed that it will be possible to discriminate the convergent sets which converge to a single point from all other types of sets. For example, if each object of the set is formed by two not overlapping spheres of radius r, with centers A and B, by diminishing r indefinitely, and keeping A and B fixed, we would have convergence to the pair of points A and B. To eliminate the occurrence of enclosure objects formed by such detached fragments in space as the two non-overlapping spheres, Whitehead introduces the notion of "covering" which is essentially the same as in "La Theorie Relationniste de l'Espace" but is more clearly described:

The convergent set "a" will be said
to "cover" the convergent set "b,"
if every member of "a" encloses some
members of "b". . . . Thus if "a"
covers "b," every member of "a" encloses
every member of the tail-end of "b,",
starting from the largest member of "b"
which is enclosed by that member of "a".(42)

If each of the two convergent sets cover the
other, they are said to be equal. If every convergent
set that is covered by "a" is also equal to it, the
set will have punctual type of convergence, that is,
it will converge to an ideal limit which is a point.
(See Figure 5.) This is not only a <u>sufficient</u> condition
for such convergence, but it is also a <u>necessary</u> condition due to the judgment that thought-objects of
perception do not possess exact boundaries prior to
the elaboration of exact mathematical concepts of space.

But such exact determination as is
involved in the conception of an
exact spatial boundary does not seem
to belong to the true thought-object
of perception. The ascription of an
exact boundary really belongs to the
<u>transition stage of thought</u> as it
<u>passes from the thought-object</u> of
<u>science</u>. The transition from the
sense-object immediately presented
to the thought-object of perception
is historically made in a wavering
indeterminate line of thought.(43)

The underlined passage makes Whitehead's understanding
of the status of converging series of objects quite
clear. Such an exact mathematical device is not
given in perception.

Since it is possible that equal convergent
sets could converge to the same point "P" by various
routes of approximation, Whitehead uses the idea of
a "class" to define a point "P" in such a way that "P"
only includes convergent sets of the punctual type, and
the route of approximation indicated by any two of these
sets converges to identical results. The point "P" is
thus defined as the <u>class</u> formed by all the enclosure-

objects which belong to "a" or to any convergent set which is equal to "a." Whereas a point had been derived from a series of converging straight lines in the "Memoir of 1905," Whitehead now had derived a point from a series of overlapping volumes. It is this derivation of a point as a logical entity which Whitehead will use in the method of extensive abstraction.

Points, lines, planes

The sole use of these derived points, Whitehead states, is to facilitate the employment of the principle of convergence to simplicity which now can be carried through to its ideal limit. Whitehead thought of straight lines and planes as containing infinite numbers of points. The problem of intellectually constructing these lines and planes from points can be accomplished in Whitehead's logical system by renewed applications of the principle of aggregation in much the same way as a set of first crude thought-objects of perception are aggregated into one complete thought-object of perception. Repeated judgments of the collinearity of sets of points are finally (when certain conditions of interlacing are fulfilled) aggregated in the single judgment of all the points of the groups as forming one whole collinear group. The same holds for judgments of coplanarity.

Empty space

Whitehead is dissatisfied with his development of lines and planes from points. Points, he notes, necessarily involve thought-objects of perception since they "lie within the space-extension occupied by such objects." These thought-objects are largely hypothetical and in order to complete our lines and planes, we must greatly increase the number of these hypothetical objects. This almost indiscriminate multiplication of hypothetical entities offends the author of the "Memoir of 1905." Again. Whitehead appeals to Occam's Razor to strengthen his plea for simplicity. If we were to apply Occam's principle to science, Whitehead claims that it would mean that "every use of hypothetical entities diminishes the claim of scientific reasoning to be the necessary outcome of a harmony between thought and sense-presentation." Common-sense supports this claim since most individuals

61

would balk at the conception of space as essentially
dependent on hypothetical objects which fill it. Space
is there, but is it and must it be full of these hypothetical objects? Is there any meaning to "empty space,"
that is to space not containing such hypothetical objects?

Whitehead attempts an affirmative answer to the
commonsense question of the meaning of empty space. He
does so by extending the definition of points. Up to
now, points were derived as limits of series of enclosure
objects of a certain type. These points, Whitehead now
calls by a more technical name, "material points."
A wider definition of points is now introduced which
allows points to indicate the possibilities of external
relations other than that of enclosure. Whitehead
achieves this by enlarging the geometric concept of an
ideal point in the following way. He first defines
material lines as the "complete collinear classes of
collinear points." An ideal point, then, is the set of
material lines which contain a certain material point.
In this case, the ideal point is an occupied point.
(See Figure 2.)

To achieve an unoccupied ideal point, Whitehead
considers a set of three material lines, two of which
are coplanar, the third is not. Then if we consider
the complete set of material lines such that each is
coplanar with each of the three material lines first
chosen, then the total set of lines, including the three
original ones, forms an ideal point according to the
definition in its full generality. Such an ideal point
may or may not be occupied. This ideal point, indicating
as it does the possibility of spatial relations which
has not been realized, is the point of empty space.
(See Figure 2c.) Whitehead concludes by saying that
"space as thus conceived is the thought-space of the
material world." It is to this thought-space that the
thought-objects of science are said to be directly related:

> Space as thus conceived is the exact
> formulation of the properties of the
> apparent space of the commonsense world
> of experience. It is not necessarily
> the best mode of conceiving the space
> of the physicist. The one essential
> requisite is that the correspondence
> between the commonsense world in its
> and the physicists' world in its space

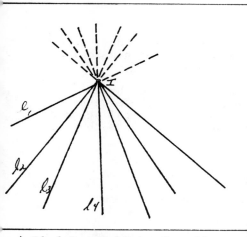

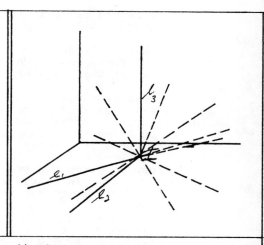

a) Ideal Occupied Point formed by a pencil of material lines

b) Ideal Occupied Point--l_1 and l_2 are coplanar.

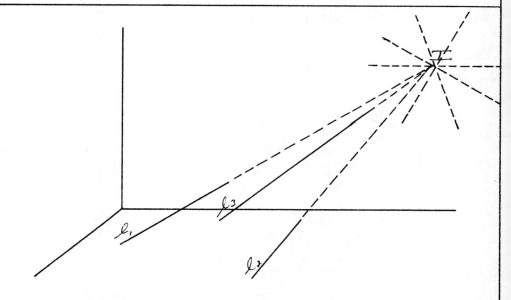

c) Ideal Unoccupied Point--Empty Space. l_1 and l_2 are coplanar; l_3 is not coplanar with l_1 and l_2 but parallel to them.

Fig. 2--Ideal Points--Occupied and Unoccupied.

space should be definite and
reciprocal.(44)

With this development of unoccupied ideal points
as points of empty space, Whitehead completes his logical
theory of space which was begun in 1914.

Let us conclude our analysis of the three
transitional essays as Whitehead concluded the essays--
with a discussion of metaphysics. Since physical science
is based on elements of thought, Whitehead admits that it
requires metaphysical analysis.

> Science only renders the metaphysical need
> more urgent. In itself it contributes
> little directly to the solution of the
> metaphysical problem. But it does con-
> tribute something, namely, the
> exposition of the fact that our
> experience of sensible apparent things
> is capable of being analyzed into a
> scientific theory, a theory not indeed
> complete, but giving every promise of
> indefinite expansion. . . . In the
> past false science has been the parent
> of bad metaphysics. After all, science
> embodies a rigorous scrutiny of one
> part of the whole evidence from which
> metaphysicians deduce their con-
> clusions.(45)

Importance of Transitional Works

Now that we have completed a study of the so-
called "transitional" works of Whitehead, let us briefly
highlight our findings. The first paper we treated as
a condition for any in-depth knowledge of Whitehead's
philosophy of space was the "Memoir of 1905."

In this memoir, which is first and foremost
a mathematical investigation, we have an excellent example
of Whitehead's axiomatic method. The concept comes first
in the order of the mind, and it was Whitehead's concern
"to exhibit concepts not inconsistent with some, if not
all, of the limited number of propositions at present
believed to be true concerning our sense perceptions."
This is an important statement since it immediately

64

separates Whitehead's work from a purely speculative mathematical treatise. Whitehead tried, in developing his later method of extensive abstraction, to ground his work on sense perceptions, gross, inadequate, and vague as such human perceptions are.

The "Memoir" also provided us with Whitehead's early views of time, space, and matter--the three primitive entities of the Classical Concept. In 1905 Whitehead had not yet espoused a relational or relative theory of time. Space and time are regarded as independent, and Whitehead gives no thought to deriving them from something more basic--similar to his derivation of points from linear objective reals. On the contrary, he posits "instants of time" as ultimate existents in every concept. With space and matter, however, the story is different. In a monistic concept such as Concept V--which Whitehead seems to prefer because of the principle of Occam's Razor--there is assumed only one class of entities forming the universe. Space and matter become properties of these entities. Matter becomes a mode of relating a point of space to an instant of time. Points of space are complexes of the linear objective reals and by the method of interpoints and the relation of intersection, spatial position is the possibility of a class of entities occupying the same position.

Whitehead's concern "to exhibit concepts not inconsistent with some, if not all, of the limited number of propositions at present believed to be true concerning our sense perceptions" gives evidence that in accordance with modern model theory, it is safe to judge the mathematical concepts of the material world set forth in the "Memoir" as mathematical models. Propositions concerning the physical world assumed to be true on the basis of sense perception would form the theory; whereas the mathematical concepts would form the model of this theory--a possible realization in which all valid statements of the theory are satisfied.

By 1914 Whitehead had adopted the relational theory of space and attempted to provide a mathematical model for it in "La Theorie Relationniste de l'Espace." Whitehead, distinguishing the apparent space of sense perception from the physical space of science, claims that there does exist a relation or correspondence between apparent objects immediately perceived by a subject and a complex of relations among physical objects in physical space. The nature of this correspondence will be undertaken by Whitehead only in his later works, particularly Process and Reality. Furthermore, science can make progress only (1) by making provisions for an approximative interpretation of its exact theorems, and (2) by replacing for the unstable objects of apparent space the more permanent scientific objects of physical space. Whitehead's acceptance of the infinite divisibility hypothesis for mathematical convenience and his acknowledgements that the principle of convergence to a conceptual limit does not apply simply to the world of apparent objects are worthy of note since several charges levied by his critics concern these very issues.

The three essays, "Space, Time, and Relativity," "The Organisation of Thought," and "The Anatomy of Some Scientific Ideas," can be thought of as philosophical completion of the "Memoir of 1905" insofar as they supply an analysis of perception and its relation to science which the Memoir neglected.

Several important themes are manifested in these essays; two in particular are important to us since they will occur repeatedly in Whitehead's future philosophy of science. These themes are: (1) the element of "thought" in Whitehead's analysis of perception (the element which bestows definiteness and demarcation), and (2) the importance of logical inference in science and perception.

Whitehead still adheres to the "class" theory of objects which he defines as classes of perceptions. Out perceptual experience is fragmentary in relation to the conceptual objects obtained by logical constructions. As far as science is concerned, "thoughts are facts and facts are thoughts." The perception of crude primary thoughts is called "sense-presentation." Secondary thoughts are derived or constructed from these primary thoughts. Perception, therefore, involves more than sense-presentation.

The difference between thoughts and thought-objects should be carefully noted. Thought-objects seem to have the same characteristics as the perceptual object of PNK and CN.(46) Whitehead's idea of sense perception involves more than the immediately given. It contains imaginative processes which provide aspects of perceptual

66

objects that are not purely given. Causality is also part of sense perception for Whitehead. The intelligible character of thought-objects of perception cannot be overstressed. Only by understanding this may we be able to justify his method of extensive abstraction. This method is slowly being shaped by means of the principle of convergence, enclosure, "covering" relation, and material points. We must also notice that Whitehead now rejects instants as ultimate entities. They have been replaced by durations.

The relations of space and time are derived from the relations of sense-objects especially the relation of whole-and-part which is a directly presented relation. Point-objects of time and space are not direct sense-presentations but hypothetical thought-objects. A distinction is made between sense-space and sense-time and thought-space and thought-time. The latter involve points and instants.

By means of the principle of convergence, Whitehead derives points of space. Similarly, instants of time are derived from a set of one-dimensional enclosure objects. The resulting definition of a point is a hypothetical thought-object of perception empirically based on the spatial and temporal whole-and-part relation of extended objects. Material lines (complete collinear classes of collinear points) are used to arrive at ideal points which may or may not be occupied. Pure geometry is now derived from a relational theory of space grounded on perceivable sense-objects. The theory of interpoints has been given a perceptual basis.

With this epistemological completion of the "Memoir of 1905" and "La Théorie Relationniste de l'Espace," Whitehead is ready to launch into a thoroughly detailed philosophy of nature which, in part at least, represents a synthesis of his thinking from 1898 to 1920.

NOTES

1. Victor Lowe and Wolfe Mays have treated the "Memoir" in scholarly fashion; Lowe has tried to trace its influence on Whitehead's later philosophy and Mays has given a summary of the work in his article, "The Relevance of 'On Mathematical Concepts of the Material World' to Whitehead's Philosophy," The Relevance of Whitehead, Ed. Ivor Leclerc (London: George Allen & Unwin Ltd., 1961), pp. 157-75. Hereafter, this particular article by Mays will be referred to as Mays, "On MC."

2. MC, N&G, p. 11.

3. A serial relation is similar to the relation which generates the negative and positive real numbers.

4. Wolfe Mays observes in "On MC" that the essential and extraneous relations would seem to be the forerunners of the essential and contingent relations of Whitehead's later philosophy. In his later work, the essential relations relate events to events; contingent relations, objects to events. See p. 239.

5. These definitions are logically independent of any axioms concerning the funcamental relations, though their convenience and importance are dependent upon such axioms. MC, N&G, p. 17.

6. In projective geometry, they can be interchanged.

7. MC, N&G, p. 26.

8. By varying the essential relation, the resulting geometry can be made non-Euclidean.

9. MC, N&G, p. 28.

10. Bertrand Russell, The Principles of Mathematics (London: George Allen & Unwin Ltd., 1903) p. 440

11. Wolfe Mays draws a comparison between the endless lines of force and durations which have no maximum or minimum extent. If his analogy holds, the totality of linear reals taken as a system will, like the lines of

force constituting the material world, form a field or a continuum.

12. He explains this furhter in "Anatomy of Some Scientific Ideas."

13. MC, N&G, p. 35.

14. Wolfe Mays compares this definition of a point with Leibniz's idea of place from which the notion of space arises. Leibniz defines "same place" as objects having the same relationship to other objects. This bears some resemblance to the similarity of position in a relation of MC.

15. Mays feels that Concept V is not a result of purely logical deliberations but a reference to electro-magnetic theory.

16. Patrick Suppes, "A Comparison of the Meaning and Uses of Models in Mathematics and the Empirical Sciences," The Concept and the Role of the Model in Mathematics and Natural and Social Sciences ("Proceedings of the Colloquium sponsored by the Division of Philosophy of Sciences of the International Union of History and Philosophy of Sciences"; (Dordrecht, Holland: D. Reidel Publishing Company, 1961), pp. 163-176. Hereafter, this article will be referred to by the author's surname only, and the volume will be called Model in Mathematics.

17. MC, N&G, p. 82.

18. "Axioms of Projective Geometry," (1906), "Axioms of Descriptive Geometry," (1907). A condensed account of these two tracts is found in Whitehead's article on "The Axioms of Geometry," (1910), Encyclopedia Britannica, Vol. XI, Div. VII of "Geometry." This latter is reprinted in Science and Philosophy (New York: Philosophical Library, 1948). This latter publication will hereafter be referred to as SP.

19. RTS, p. 430. (Italics mine.) The letter "s" is used instead of the Greek "sigma" for typographical reasons.

20. That is (1) "a" is part of itself, (2) if "a" is part of "b" and "b" is part of "c" then "a" is part of "c," and (3) if "a" is part of "b" then "b" is not a

part of "a" in apparent and physical space unless "a" and "b" are identical. If they are identical, Whitehead adds further technical restrictions which give us, practically speaking, the doctrine of Leibniz on the identity of indiscernibles.

21. Whitehead notes that in MC a method of defining these geometrical entities independent of this relation was given, and that many modes of definition are possible. It is very essential that they be found so that the methods best suited to the perspective facts (for apparent space) or the scientific hypotheses (for physical space) can be developed.

22. This he does in later works beginning with "The Anatomy of Some Scientific Ideas."

23. RTS, p. 446.

24. Roman letters are used instead of the Greek for typographical reasons.

25. RTS, p. 447. (Italics mine.)

26. RTS, p. 448

27. "Space, Time, and Relativity," AE. p. 157. Hereafter this essay will be referred to as STR.

28. Hereafter called OT.

29. Hereafter called ASI,

30. For such a detailed study, see Fernando Molina, "Whitehead's Realism in Relation to the Problem of Perception" (unpublished Ph.D. Dissertation, Department of Philosophy, Yale University, 1959).

31. STR, AE. p. 165

32. Ibid., p. 164.

33. ASI, AE. pp. 125-26. (Italics mine.)

34. ASI, AE. p. 131.

35. Ibid.

36. This apparent bifurcation of science and meta-physics is a recurring theme during this period of Whitehead's writings. However, just as the bothersome problem of perception in the "Memoir of 1905" and RTS forced him to develop an epistemological theory, the problems of the philosophy of science period drove Whitehead into forming his metaphysics, which in later years he judged as being indispensable to science.

37. ASI, AE, p. 132. Thought-objects of perception take on the space-relations and time-relations of their component sense-objects. These relations make up the "thought time of perception" and the "thought space of perception."

38. ASI, AE, p. 135.

39. ASI, AE, p. 136. We have used "a" instead of the Greek "alpha" for typographical reasons. (Italics mine.)

40. The similarity to the property of "inclusion" in RTS is quite obvious.

41. This is the predecessor of "abstractive classes" in the Method of Extensive Abstraction.

42. ASI, AE, p. 141. Again, Roman letters have been used for the Greek.

43. ASI, AE, p. 142. (Italics mine.)

44. OT, AE, p. 118. (Italics mine.)

45. ASI, AE, p. 153.

46. Schmidt believes that this would refute Northrop who says that Whitehead cannot succeed in deriving scientific concepts from sense-presentation alone. Northrop's error ("Whitehead's Philosophy of Science," Schilpp, pp. 191-205) rests on a misinterpretation of Whitehead's unique meaning of sense perception. Paul Schmidt, Perception and Cosmology in Whitehead's Philosophy (New Brunswick: Rutgers University Press, 1967), p. 21.

CHAPTER III

EARLY THEORY OF SPACE AND TIME

The transition has now been made. The mathe-
maticial-logician is now a full-fledged natural
philosopher ready to elaborate and develop his views in
lectures, articles, and books. The three major volumes
of Whitehead's philosophy of nature period are: An
Enquiry Concerning the Principles of Natural Knowledge
(1919), The Concept of Nature (1920),and The Principle
of Relativity (1922). The highlight or climax of these
three volumes (often referred to as a unity by being
called "the 1920 books") is the method of extensive
abstraction. However, Whitehead's early theory of perception is also contained in these works as a prolegomena
to the method. As such an indispensable part of the
three volumes, the theory of events and objects which
is developed in detail by Whitehead will also be dealt
with in this paper. Only by a true grasp of Whitehead's
thoughts on sense perception as they developed from the
transition essays of 1915-1917 can one appreciate
Whitehead's attempt to derive the entities of science
from the empirically given.

New Critique of Classical Concept

Once again, Whitehead begins a new, major
treatise with an old theme--a criticism of the Classical
Concept. Now, however, we note a definite change of
emphasis from the "Memoir of 1905." The criticism found
in the latter was purely logical; in Principles of
Natural Knowledge, Whitehead's primary concern is the
lack of agreement between the classical cosmology and
observable nature.(1) The Newtonian World View, as we
have noted previously. describes the world in terms of
instants of time, timeless euclidean space, and extended
material particles in space. The extended material is

composed of a multiplicity of discrete entities which,
though extended, are by the very reason of their dis-
creteness, disconnected. Some modification of the
Classical World-View must be made to allow for such
physical quantities as change, velocity, and momentum.
It is quite difficult to try to explain change within
the confines of Newton's philosophy of nature. Change
at a durationless instant is a very difficult conception. How can one possibly explain velocity without
referring to the past as well as to the future? Change,
according to Whitehead is "essentially the importation
of the past and of the future into the immediate fact
embodied in the durationless present instant."(2)
This view of change demands that the ultimate facts of
science cannot be found at durationless instants of
time. The Classical Concept fails in its explanations
in the fields of physics and biology; therefore, a new,
more radical philosophy must be constructed which will
be based on our experiences of a changing, progressing
world.

In physics, the assumption of discrete, disconnected, spatially extended bodies leads to great
difficulties in explaining the transmission of stress
across the boundaries of contiguous bits of matter.
The problem is this: if we have discrete bits of matter,
what do we mean when we say they are "in contact?" No
two points are ever in contact since points have no
length, breadth, or width. Therefore, we cannot say
that transmission of stress takes place on the boundary
points of the bodies concerned. Then we are forced to
say that the stress acts on the bulk of material enclosed within the boundaries. But to say this is to
assert the existence of infinitely small volumes. But
mathematics has shown that there are no such things!
The Classical Concept with its points of space and
discrete bits of matter is totally inadequate to explain
the physical fact of stress across a surface.

In biology, the Classical Concept fares no
better. The biological concept of an organism as a unity
which functions and enjoys spatio-temporal extension
cannot be expressed in terms of material particles
existing at an instant. Functioning takes time; it does
not take place at an instant.

Whitehead now begins his venturous undertaking

of explaining all physical and biological facts in terms
of new ultimate facts of nature instead of the three
traditional ones of spatial points, instants of time,
and discrete material particles. He wants to replace
the traditional view of space and time with one which
treats of them not as natural entities themselves but
as derivative from natural entities.

Whitehead chooses as his ultimate natural
entity the spatio-temporal event. An event is a happening; it is what we experience immediately in perception.
What we perceive is not an "instant" or a point. Rather
we perceive events which take time and do possess some
spatial extension as well. Events can overlap or extend
over smaller events. The event which is all today contains or envelops the event which is this morning.
Spatio-temporal relations are properties of these events.
How does Whitehead go about deriving his philosophy of
space and time as a philosophy of coherent relations
between events? He begins by an examination of nature
and the process of perception.

Upon examination of Nature, Whitehead finds
it to be diversified. Two major methods of diversification are classification of Nature into events and into
sense-data (objects). Whichever mode of diversification
is chosen (and Whitehead utilizes both) the entities
revealed are called "elements," and these elements are
related to each other. When elements of the same mode
of diversification are related, we call such a relation
a "homogeneous" one. "Heterogeneous" relations, then,
would relate natural elements of different types.

Relations play an important part in Whitehead's
philosophy of nature. His love for the logic of relations
is never lost; it is his favorite tool as well as his most
powerful technique. Since Whitehead uses the term
"significance" to mean the relatedness of things, before
we advance any further in our discussion, it will be to
our benefit to say a brief word on the meaning of
"significance." Whitehead describes it this way:

> "Significance" is the relatedness of
> things. To say that significance is
> experience, is to affirm that perceptual
> knowledge is nothing else than an
> apprehension of the relatedness of
> things, namely of things

in their relations and as related. Certainly if we commence with a knowledge of
things, and then look around for their
relations we shall not find them. . . .
But then we are quite mistaken in thinking
that there is a possible knowledge of
things as unrelated. It is thus out of
the question to start with a knowledge of
things antecedent to a knowledge of their
relation. The so-called properties of
things can always be expressed as their
relatedness to other things unspecified,
and natural knowledge is exclusively concerned with relatedness.(3)

Whitehead is saying that we know things only as related
to other things. Even our perception of things is a
relation between the perceiver and the thing known.
What's more, our perception of natural events and natural
objects is a perception from <u>within</u> <u>nature</u>--not an
awareness impartially from without. According to Whitehead perception involves a percipient object (the
perceiver), a percipient event (temporal portion of the
perceiver's mind), the complete all-embracing event which
is all nature simultaneous with the percipient event, and
the particular events which are perceived as parts of the
complete event called a "duration."

        Perception is active insofar as the percipient
has the direct knowledge that its very being is in the
formation of its natural relations. This is what Whitehead meant by knowledge from within nature. We, as a
percipient event which endures, are one with nature insofar as nature also "advances." We are both "in the
making."

        This passage of nature--or, in other
        words, its creative advance--is its
        fundamental characteristic: the tra-
        ditional Newtonian concept is an
        attempt to catch nature without its
        passage.(4)

How does Whitehead explain the "creative advance" of Nature?
The answer is found in his theory of events and their relations to one another

Events

A relation always requires relata. "Events are the relata of the fundamental homogeneous relation of 'extension'." Both time and space spring from this relation. Events (like the sense-objects and thought-objects of the three transitional essays) extend over other events which are their parts, and every event is extended over by other events of which it is a part. Thus, there are no maximum or minimum events. The whole-to-part inclusion relationship developed as far back as 1914 and the infinite divisibility hypothesis can be seen reflected in this definition. Now these principles are applied to events, and time and space are considered as derivatives or characteristics of the relation of the extension of events (and not as properties of extension as was previously believed).

Events are "happenings" in nature; they are matters of fact involved in the becomingness of nature. The philosophy of process is emerging at last from its mathematical cacoon.

An actual event is thus divested of all
possibility. It is what does become
in nature. It can never happen again:
for essentially it is just itself,
there and then. An event is just what
it is, and is just how it is related
and it is nothing else. (5)

Events never change as Nature develops. They pass into some other larger events of which they become parts. Thus, the passage of events is spatio and temporal extension in the making. It is what it is, when it is, and where it is. It is there and not here (or vice-versa). Events are concrete, particular, subject to passage, neither permanent nor changeable, and composed of parts which are other events. They comprise nature insofar as nature exhibits spatiotemporal aspects, and they are specific and unambiguous in spatiotemporal location.

Perception of Events

        We are aware of events passing into larger
events. This awareness Whitehead calls "perception."
"Perception is an awareness of events." In the process
of perception, one event (or group of events) plays a
dominant role and that is the percipient event. It is
not easy to explain what Whitehead means by the percipient event. We so easily slip into referring to an
event by having recourse to the object which character-
izes it. If I am at present perceiving a blue color,
my body is what Whitehead terms the "percipient object."
The percipient event would be the existence or endurance
of my mind during the process--my "mental happening."
My mental happening now, together with the whole of
nature as a background of possible discernible events,
constitutes a complete whole of nature which Whitehead
labels a "duration." Durations have a very technical
meaning in Whitehead's philosophy. They are events
that have no spatial boundaries; that is they extend
indefinitely in space. However, they do have finite
events as their parts and are temporally bounded.
(See Figure 3.) In other words a duration is a temporal
slab of all of nature. Today's duration would be the
event occurring all over Nature (spatially indefinite)
from midnight last night to midnight tonight. The
duration from 11:30 A.M. to 11:31 A.M. would be the
event occurring throughout all Nature in that specific
minute. Since I, a percipient event, also exist during
that minute, I am part of the duration.

        Since a duration is a concrete slab of nature,
finite in temporal breadth but unlimited in spatial extent, and since Whitehead later defines space and time
in terms of durations, this definition of duration, if
taken literally, is circular. Robert Palter defends
Whitehead on this matter by beginning with another definition of the term which does not employ the concepts of
space and time. Palter defines a duration as "a certain
whole of nature which is limited only by the property of
being a simultaneity."(7) "Simultaneity" is a crucial term
which Whitehead explains by stating that this relation
is directly given in perception by reference to the
doctrine of significance. By focusing attention upon
one particular mode of significance--the indefinitely
extended projection of the spatial boundaries of a single
specious present--Palter believes one arrives at the
notion of a duration. For example, as I sit at my desk

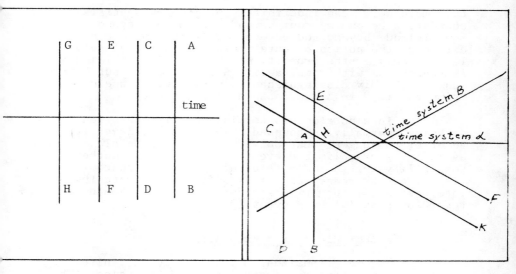

Fig. 3--The slab of nature forming a duration is limited in its
temporal dimension and unlimited in its spatial dimensions. Thus it
presents a finite time and infinite space. For example let the
horizontal line represent the time; and assume nature to be spatially
one-dimensional, so that an unlimited vertical line in the diagram
represents space at an instant. Then the area between the unlimited
parallel lines AB and HG represents a duration. Also the area between
CD and EF represents another duration which is extended over by the
duration bounded by AB and HG. But in figure 2 we have assumed only one
time-system, which is the Newtonian hypothesis. Suppose there are many
time-systems and consider two such systems α and β. These are represented
by two lines inclined to each other. A duration of time-system α is
represented by the area between AB and CD, and a duration of time-system
β is represented by the area between EF and HK. Two such durations
necessarily intersect and also can neither completely extend over the other.

These diagrams are crude illustrations of some properties of
durations and are in many respects misleading. . . .(6)

79

this morning, I can indefinitely project my spatial
boundaries beyond my room beyond the house, beyond
Long Island, beyond and beyond. This is how we can
arrive at the notion of duration as the whole of nature
limited only by the property of simultaneity. "Immediacy"
is synonymous with simultaneity for Whitehead, but both
must be sharply distinguished from Einstein's use of
"simultaneity" in his principle of relativity.

In a note on his terminology of a duration
as being spatially "unbounded," Whitehead believes it is
an error to suggest that only durations can be classified
as infinite or unlimited events.(8) There is another
possibility for an infinite event. An event spatially
finite, but by reason of its significance, stretching
into past and future time without limit also should be
regarded as an infinite event.(9)

Cogredience and Extension

Two relations that may hold between finite
events and durations are cogredience and extension. The
latter has already been mentioned and will be discussed
in detail in the development of the method of extensive
abstraction. The relation of cogredience relates the
percipient event to the duration of which it is a part.
An event is said to be cogredient with a duration when
it is spatially fixed, and temporally touches both
boundaries of a duration. Whitehead explains it in this
manner:

> An event can be cogredient with only
> one duration. To have this relation
> to the duration it must be temporally
> present throughout the duration and
> exhibit one specific meaning of 'here.'(10)

Let us take the illustration of a percipient
sitting at a desk. I am sitting at my desk (the "here"
position) this morning writing this page. The percipient
event which is the state of my mind during this time--
say from 11:00 A.M. to 11:30 A.M.--is cogredient with
the duration which is all of nature during the same
time interval. What constitutes cogredience is the
sameness of the temporal boundaries and the unique spatial
position of the percipient event. While an event can be

cogredient with only one duration, a duration can have
many events cogredient with it. (There are perhaps many
other perceiving events also enduring between 11:00 A.M.
and 11:30 A.M. this morning.) Cogredience is a condition for a percipient event which makes possible
unequivocal meanings to the experience "here" and "now."
Not only is cogredience necessary because of its role in
the theory of perception as the relation between the
perceiving event and all of Nature, but it is also the
relation of <u>absolute position</u> within a duration. As
such it is fundamental to the derivative ideas of motion
and rest. Rest occurs when there is cogredience between
an event and a duration; motion, when there is no such
relation present. If I sit at my desk from 11:00 A.M.
to 11:15 A.M. then I am not cogredient with the duration
which has as its boundaries 11:00 A.M. and 11:30 A.M.
This means that either of two things has occurred.
Either I have ceased to exist as a percipient event in
which case my temporal boundary does not extend as late
as 11:30 A.M. Or, I must have changed my fixed spatial
position at 11:15 A.M. In other words, at 11:15 A.M. I
must have moved from my position at my desk. I am not
at rest during the larger duration with boundaries extending from 11:00 A.M. to 11:30 A.M. since my spatial
position during that half-hour duration was not fixed.

It is the percipient event with its unequivocal
meaning of "here" and "now" which can be said "defines"
the duration with which it is cogredient. The <u>unique</u>
standpoint of a percipient event in its associated duration
is different from that of any other finite event (percipient or otherwise) cogredient with the duration. This
leads to what Whitehead terms a theory of "absolute
position."

"Cogredience is the relation of absolute
position within a duration." At first we may be inclined
to think that a theory of absolute position means that
Whitehead, though espousing a relative theory of space,
is inadvertently speaking as an absolutist. But the
assumption that a relative theory of space cannot include
a theory of absolute position is an error caused by the
failure to admit alternative definitions of absolute
position:

       Now you cannot have a theory of
    rest without in some sense admitting
    a theory of absolute position. It is

usually assumed that relative space
implies that there is no absolute
position. This is, according to my
creed, a mistake. The assumption arises
from the failure to make another distinction; namely, that there may be
alternative definitions of absolute
position. This possibility enters with
the admission of alternative time-
systems.(11)

Since there is always the possibility of different percipient events having correspondingly different meanings
of "simultaneity," Whitehead holds that there may very
well be alternative definitions of absolute position.
The outcome of this is the notion of alternative time-
systems in nature. Among the alternative systems nature
offers, Whitehead claims that there is one with a duration
which yields the best average of cogredience for all the
subordinate parts of the percipient event. This best
"average" duration is the whole of nature posited by
sense-awareness.

. . . amid the alternative time-systems
which nature offers there will be one
with a duration giving the best
average of cogredience for all the
subordinate parts of the percipient
event. This duration will be the
whole of nature which is the terminus
posited by sense-awareness. Thus the
character of the percipient event
determines the time-system immediately
evident in nature--or, in other words,
as the percipient mind in its passage
correlates itself with the passage of
the percipient event into another percipient event--the time-system correlated
with the percipience of that mind may
change.(12)

If we grant (with Palter) Whitehead's basic
assumption that "time is a stratification of nature,"
it follows that two events simultaneous for one mode of
stratification may not be simultaneous for another mode.
Scientists initially became aware of the possibility of
alternative time-systems with the results of ether-drift

experiments such as the Michelson-Morley Experiment
(1881) and Einstein's formulation of the special theory
of relativity (1905).

> The essence of this structure space-
> time is that it is stratified in many
> different ways by different time-systems.
> This is a very peculiar idea which is
> the product of the speculations of the
> last fifteen years or so. We owe the
> whole conception notably to Einstein.
> I do not agree with his way of handling
> his discovery. But I have no doubt as
> to its general correctness. It is at
> first sight somewhat of a shock to think
> that other beings may slice nature into
> time-sections in a different way to what
> we do. In fact we have differences among
> ourselves which luckily are quite imper-
> ceptible. However if we allow this
> possibility we not only explain many
> modern delicate experiments, but we
> also obtain explanations of what we
> mean by the spatial extension in three
> dimensions, and by planes and straight
> lines, and parallels and right-angles.
> We also obtain definite meaning for the
> matching which is the basis of our
> congruence. The explanation is too
> sweeping to be put aside. Our whole
> geometry is merely the expression of the
> ways in which different events are im-
> plicated in different time-systems.(13)

The basic difference between Whitehead's view
of relativity and Einstein's is their choice of ultimate
entities. For Whitehead, these ultimates are events:
for Einstein they are bodily objects. Whitehead also
wished to derive a general theory of relativity from his
philosophy of nature without having any recourse to
specifics about clocks, measuring rods, and the velocity
of light in vacuo. Such special characteristics should
not be essential formulations of a natural philosophy.
Instead, what Whitehead wants (and needs for his theory
of relativity) is the mere possibility of alternative
space-time systems in nature because such a possibility

is given to sense-perception.(14)

Constants of Externality

Though an event has many characteristics,
Whitehead considers six from which the concepts of space,
time, and material arise. The six characteristics
answer the fundamental questions, "Which?" "What?" "How?"
"When?" "Where?" "Whither?" When we judge an event to
be exterior or external to us, we have invested it with
certain characteristics which Whitehead terms the
"constants of externality." These constants are "those
characteristics of a perceptual experience which it
possesses when we assign to it the property of being an
observation of the passage of external nature."(15)

Because events appear as "indefinite entities
without clear demarcations," and because the responses
engendered by the six preceding questions reveal a set
of determinate things, we are faced with a difficulty.(16)
No event exhibits definite, spatio-temporal limits in
awareness, but it is only through a continuous transition
that demarcations are assigned to the event by what Whitehead unfortunately calls an "arbitrary act of thought."

This demarcation of events is the
first difficulty which arises in
applying rational thought to experience.
In perception no event exhibits definite
spatio-temporal limits. A continuity of
transition is essential. The definition
of an event by assignment of demarcations
is an arbitrary act of thought corresponding to no perceptual experience. Thus
it is a basal assumption, essential for
ratiocination relating to perceptual
experience, that there are definite
entities which are events; though in
practice our experience does not enable
us to identify any such subject of thought,
as discriminated from analogous subjects
slightly more or slightly less.(17)

A word about Whitehead's use of the term "thought"
in the above passage is a necessity. At first glance it
may seem that Whitehead agrees with those of his critics
who claim that a definite demarcation of an event implicitly

84

requires the very notion of a point which the method of extensive abstraction proposes to define. This is not so. During this period of Whitehead's writings, "cogitation," "thought," "instinctive judgment" are all synonymous terms and are part of the complete process of perception. The assumption of the exact demarcation of events is not an importation into perception from a higher source of knowledge such as conceptual thought or ratiocination.(18) Thus when we use the words "thought" or "cogitation" to mean "demarcation" we shall always use quotation marks to remind the reader that Whitehead's use of the words in this matter is a peculiar one.

This transition from awareness of factors (events) to the "cogitation" of entities is referred to by Whitehead in his statement of the first constant of externality. "The belief that what has been apprehended as a continuum, is a potentially definite complex of entities for knowledge."

Let us take a simple illustration. The events taking place in Cambodia recently have vague spatial and temporal boundaries. It is only by the process of perceptual demarcation that we can say when the "Cambodia War" began and to what part of the world it is restricted. Our first awareness of the happenings in that country was blurred, indefinite, vague. It required "thought" (instinctive demarcations) to achieve definiteness.

The second constant of externality is the relation of extension which holds between events. Whitehead has been developing this relation of "extending over" since 1914. To restate: an event "x" may extend over event "y." Then "y" is a part of "x." Whitehead states that most of the concepts of space and time arise from the empirically determined properties of this relation. "Every element of space and time (as conceived in science) is an abstract entity formed out of this relation of extension. The manner in which this is accomplished is through the method of extensive abstraction, a determinate logical procedure. This method performs the transition from approximation to exact thought by systematizing the instinctive procedure of habitual perceptual experience. It is a formulation of the law by which in ordinary life, man achieves the simplicity of relations among events by considering events sufficiently restricted in spatio-temporal extension. The details of such a system will be considered in the following chapter. For now, what interests us is the theory of perception which is its foundation.

The third, fourth, and fifth constants of externality pertain to the awareness of a duration, the complete whole of nature, and to percipient events. The fifth constant is the fact of the definite station of a percipient event within its duration, the definite univocal meaning to the relation "here" within the duration. In Process and Reality the percipient event becomes the "seat" of a focal region. For example, the occurrence of my room for the extent of three minutes defines an event which defines a certain duration having a temporal stretch of three minutes also. My act, of awareness of this occurrence is another event of the same temporal limit-- three minutes. Hence, the percipient event (my act of awareness), a finite event belonging to a duration, is by reason of the sameness of the temporal limitation, at rest within the duration. If it were not at rest, the meaning of "here-present" would be vague. Thus, the percipient event is cogredient with the duration.

The sixth constant of externality Whitehead calls the "Community of Nature." This constant arises from the fragmentary nature of perception and gives rise to the notions of continuity and publicity in nature. Because of the extension of events and the property of their extending over other events, nature is spatially continuous. Of course, this continuity would never result if events had exact, definite, spatial boundaries, but as we know, they do not-- such boundaries are a result of an act of "cogitation." The passage of events--one duration overlapping another ad infinitum reveals the temporal continuity of nature. How, though, does this continuity achieve a public status? Different observers have different acts of awareness, and each act of awareness involves a complex of related events in relation to the percipient event. Whitehead can solve this problem by recalling his statement that a percipient event defines a duration which involves other events among which are possibly other percipient events. These other percipient events could define the same duration. Thus,

it is the possible _identity_ _of_ _durations_ _by_ _various_
percipient _events_ which provides a community of nature
for all awareness. But this is basically a metaphysical question, and as such, it is dismissed with
no further explanation since Whitehead feels it is
unnecessary for the purposes of science.

The constants of externality, dealing as
they do with events, interrelate with each other making
it impossible to describe any one of them in complete
isolation from the others. Palter, reflecting on this
complex interrelationship of the constants, rebukes
those critics of Whitehead who "find circularities in
the description of each constant."(19) They are look-
ing for strict definitions where none is possible.

Objects

The diversification of nature into types of
events is not the only possible method. Since nature
presents us also with objects, Whitehead deals with
them in detail. Objects are characteristics or ingredients of events. They are only indirectly in space
and time by the process known as "ingression." Objects
make possible not only the comparison of events but
also their demarcation:

> The demarcation of events, the splitting
> of nature up into parts is effected by the
> objects which we recognize as their in-
> gredients. The discrimination of nature
> is the recognition of objects amid
> passing events.(20)

An object necessarily requires a corresponding
event, but an event need not have an object ingredient
in it since Whitehead allows for "empty space."

> The point which I want to make now is
> that being the situation of a well-marked
> object is not an inherent necessity for an
> event. . . . something is always going on
> everywhere, even in so-called empty
> space.(21)

Nathaniel Lawrence believes Whitehead is

inconsistent in his view that an event need not have an object ingredient in it.(22) He cites the following passage to support his opinion, claiming that in it Whitehead asserts that events do require objects:

> Objects are entities recognised as appertaining to events; they are the recognita amid events. Events are named after the objects involved in them and according to how they are involved.(23)

Lawrence attempts to reconcile this statement with Whitehead's view of empty space by extending Whitehead's doctrine of significance as the relatedness of things. Lawrence would treat the eventful character of empty space "as that portion of an event in which the ingression of objects is of such slight insistence as to be of negligible importance." The ingression of an object may be of minimum influence in its neighborhood, says Lawrence, who cites Whitehead on this point:

> An object is ingredient throughout its neighborhood, and its neighborhood is indefinite. Also the modification of events by ingression is susceptible of quantitative differences. Finally therefore we are driven to admit that each object is in some sense ingredient throughout nature; though its ingression may be quantitatively irrelevant in the expression of our individual experiences.(24)

Now all of this is a misinterpretation of Whitehead on the part of Lawrence. Because Whitehead states that events are named after the objects involved in them, he does not mean that events require objects. There is no inconsistency in the above passages. Whitehead's theory of empty space is quite clear; he does not mean space in which the ingression of objects is of negligible quantity.

Classification of Objects

Objects are classified by Whitehead in different ways. He broadly divides them into uniform objects

88

and non-uniform objects. Uniform objects are those
which require no minimum of time-lapse in the situation
events.

> 'Uniform' objects are objects with a
> certain smoothness in their temporal
> relations, so that they require no
> minimum quantum of time-lapse in the
> events which are their situations. These
> are objects which can be said to exist
> 'at a given moment.' For example, a tune
> is not a uniform object; but a chair, as
> ordinarily recognized, is such an
> object.(25)

If an object is a uniform object, then one can diminish
without limit the time span of the event without destroy-
ing the full representation of the object in the event.
Whitehead gives the example of a "tune" as a non-uniform
object. If one repeatedly diminishes the time span it
is quite easy to see that one destroys the tune--it is
successively whittled down until all that is left is one
note or a part of that last note. A tune, a song, requires a certain amount of time lapse for its existence
as a whole melody.

Whitehead also classifies objects into eight
different types: percipient objects, rhythms, sense-
objects, perceptual objects, physical objects, scientific
objects, material objects, and figures. Of these, the
first two are non-uniform, but the remaining six types
may be either uniform or non-uniform. It is not necessary for the scope of this paper to study the above types
of objects with the exception of the scientific object
which is the most problematic of them all.

Scientific Objects

The demand for simplicity and permanence leads
Whitehead to the concept of scientific objects. These
are not attainable by sense-awareness directly but are
intellectually inferred by a sort of insight into
nature. They result by an attempt of reason to explain
the causal character of events. Scientific objects
appear in Whitehead's early theory both to be within
the mind (which as Whitehead once stated is not in
nature). These two different meanings of "scientific

object" Nathaniel Lawrence labels the "realistic" and
"conceptualistic "--strains which run through all of
Whitehead's writing of this period. James Wright Felt
agrees with Lawrence and suggests that Whitehead actually
uses "scientific object" in two different senses: the
denoted sense referring to the causal characters within
nature and the denotive sense referring to our imperfect
mental conceptions of these permanences.(26) The only
way both these aspects can be satisfactorily correllated
to avoid a bifurcation of nature is to analyze the intellectual inference involved. Felt feels that since
such an analysis is outside nature, Whitehead's philosophy of nature has failed by reason of his exclusion of
mind from nature. Though Whitehead does undeniably
make the statement that "nature is closed to mind,"(27)
the entire context of his natural philosophy indicates
that he did not mean by this that mind and nature were
mutually exclusive, but that nature did not need mind
for its order or rationale. If we can accept this,
admitting that Whitehead's statements along this line
are indeed not compatible with his consequent writings,
we can proceed.

        Scientific objects include such things as
atoms and molecules. "At the present epoch the ultimate
scientific objects are electrons." The electron, though
an abstraction, is in the event but not confined to a
localized charge. An electron is a "whole field of
force," the "systematic way in which all events are modified as the expression of its ingression." An electron,
then, is both a conception and in nature.

        This view certainly has its difficulties in
the history of science which relates fundamental changes
in scientific theory. Consider, for instance, what has
happened to the concepts of a material ether (which
Whitehead says should be replaced by the concept of an
ether of events), the wave-theory of light, the atoms of
Lucretius and Hobbes. Whitehead would have to say, at
least according to Lawrence, that though these concepts
have been revised, they still are somehow in nature.
Then, by Lawrence's terms, Whitehead again is caught
in an apparent contradiction between his own insistence,
on the one hand, of the constant need for enunciation
of more adequate concepts in the development of scientific
systems, and, on the other hand, by his assurance that
objects and events are in nature. The problem here is
whether Lawrence is correct in thinking that these two

views are incompatible.

Whitehead, as a scientist and a philosopher
acutely aware of change, process, and becoming, certainly
would advocate science adopting more adequate theories
to explain newly discovered facts or to explain previously discovered facts more simply. This does not
necessitate Whitehead nullifying his view that somehow,
scientific objects are in nature. The facts which the
concept of a material ether inadequately attempted to
explain are in nature, but these very facts can now be
explained more accurately by a new scientific concept--
an ether of events. The facts which the wave theory of
light attempted to explain are still in nature, but
because of the discovery of other facts (photo-electric
effect, etc.) the wave theory is found to be inadequate,
and a new theory involving new scientific objects such
as quanta is replacing or at least supplementing the
wave theory. But the facts in nature are still the
same. Scientific objects are abstractions from these
facts. This reconciliation of Whitehead's statement
that scientific objects are not merely conceptual but
somehow in nature is one based on the totality of his
doctrine of perception.

Are scientific objects uniform or non-uniform
objects? Again Whitehead's thoughts on this subject
undergo modifications. In Principles of Natural
Knowledge Whitehead asserts that though the ultimate
scientific objects such as electrons and positive electric charges are uniform objects, the quantum theory
may require the assumption of non-uniform ultimate
scientific objects. In the same work, however, he
states that the non-uniformity of molecules is the
reason we know them as exhibiting a rhythm. By the
time Concept of Nature was published, one year later,
Whitehead's view had advanced from the mere admission
of the possibility of non-uniform scientific objects
to the confession of the likelihood that they must be so
regarded.

It is possible therefore that for
the existence of certain sorts of
objects, e.g. electrons, minimum quanta
of time are requisite. Some such
postulate is apparently indicated by
the modern quantum theory and it is
perfectly consistent with the doctrine
of objects maintained in these lectures.(28)

91

Lawrence believes that from Whitehead's theory of non-uniform objects, two different kinds of time emerge from the examination of nature--two types of time exhibiting different properties. In keeping with the thesis of his book; namely, that there is in Whitehead's philosophy two contradictory strains of thought--the conceptual and the realistic--he calls these "perceptual time" and "conceptual time."(29) Conceptual time is continuous and does not allow the positing of a minimal event. Perceptual time, on the other hand, is discontinuous because our experiences--successive unitary blocks, are distinguishable. Lawrence contrasts the case of a tune with that of the electron. By diminishing the event which is the situation of the tune, we do not empty the event, though the smaller the event, the fewer notes of the tune that are situated in it. With the electron, however, such is not the case, since it is an ultimate scientific object. Lawrence believes that if one attempts in thought to reduce the time span of the situation in any event, the result is not another event. We would have a slab of nature exhibiting the ingression of no object--there would be nothing to recognize. He concludes:

> Thus, whereas the definition of an
> abstractive set of events leads to
> the rejection of the possibility of
> a smaller event, the introduction
> of the idea of a non-uniform scientific
> object requires a smallest event.(30)

Lawrence believes Whitehead's difficulty lies both in his definition of an abstractive set which allows for no minimal element and in his postulation of the ingression of objects into natural events. This leads to different types of time--two kinds of conceptual time and one kind of perceptual time. What Lawrence is overlooking in all this is that Whitehead does allow for empty events. Lawrence is not admitting this possibility, but insists that every event must have an object ingredient in it. Also, Lawrence's basic thesis is one which is rendered implausible by Whitehead's acceptance of a "cogitative" constituent as an essential part of perception.

92

Refined Theory of Perception

By the time of the publication of The Principle of Relativity in 1922, Whitehead's theory of the perception of events had been expanded, developed, and refined. It now enjoyed a depth and clarity not quite apparent in the two earlier works. A study of these cevelopments will be of no small assistance to us since they represent the apex of Whitehead's philosophy of nature. By knowing Whitehead's conclusions of 1922, we can interpret more accurately by hindsight his writings of 1919 and 1920.

The second chapter of The Principle of Relativity, entitled "The Relatedness of Nature," is the best summary of Whitehead's theory of perception during the entire philosophy of nature period. Points on which he hesitated in The Concept of Nature are here answered definitely, and though there is a slight change in terminology, it is possible to trace the gradual expansion of Whitehead's thought.

In The Concept of Nature Whitehead talks about sense-perception and sense-awareness. Now he speaks of perception and awareness. Sense-awareness, we are told, is only a part of awareness--evidence that what was said in Principles of Natural Knowledge and Concept of Nature was only part of Whitehead's whole view of perception. Perception in Principle of Relativity contains more than sense-awareness; it contains "thought," "cogitation," i.e. "demarcation"--a theory we saw confusedly stated in the early books. It is as if Whitehead realized that things he said in 1920 required that sense-perception include an element of "thought."

Perception is defined in Principle of Relativity as "the consciousness of a factor when to full awareness cogitation of it as an entity is also super-added." Owing to Whitehead's original, technical vocabulary, there are several terms in this definition which require explanations. "Fact is a relationship of factors." A "fact" is Whitehead's term for "totality," the ultimate primitive which contains all relatedness and all diversification. Since it contains all contrasts, it cannot be contrasted with anything else. It cannot be an entity for cogitation since it has no individuality. Fact is not a relatum but the totality, the factuality of Nature, not in the sense of being a

93

definite aggregation or a sum of subordinate aggregates, but in the sense of an inexhaustibleness--the concreteness or embeddedness of factors. The ultimate facts of nature are events. As Whitehead puts it:

> Fact enters consciousness in a way peculiar to itself. It is not the sum of factors; it is rather the concreteness (or, embeddedness) of factors, and the concreteness of an inexhaustible relatedness among inexhaustible relata.(31)

Every factor (and sense-objects would be examples of factors) refers essentially to its relationship within fact--it has fact for its background and refers to fact in a unique way. A factor is a limitation within fact since it refers to fact canalised into a system of relata to itself. Whitehead uses the term "awareness" for consciousness of factors within fact, the discrimination of factors as they are seen in relation to other factors. Sometimes, awareness focuses more on the factor itself than its relatedness, but "full awareness" occurs only when factors are clearly apprehended and their relations to other factors are also apparent. "Cogitation" is the term now used for a further limitation--the consciousness of factors abstracted from their background of fact. A factor "cogitated" upon is called an entity. Here is Whitehead's own illustration of the difference between a factor and an entity:

> For example, the factor red refers to fact as canalised by relationships of other factors to red, and the entity red is the factor red in its capacity as a relatum in the relationship of contrast, whereby it is contrasted with green or with sound or with the moon or with the multiplication table. Thus the factor red, essentially for its being, occasions the exhibition of a special aspect of fact, and the entity red is a further limitation of this aspect. . . . Thus an entity is an abstraction from the concrete, which in its fullest sense means totality.(32)

Perception, then, is concerned with fact, factors, and entities as they function in awareness and cogitation. Before cogitation can take place there must be awareness of the factors of fact. Cogitation is the refinement and further limitation of awareness. "This awareness is crude consciousness and cogitation is refined consciousness." Cogitation and awareness are parts of the same process of perception. Now there is a clearer, more definite answer to the question posed in 1920; namely, was "thought" a part of sense-perception.

Nathaniel Lawrence believes that this inclusion of a "cogitative" element in the process of perception is a complete reversal on Whitehead's part. But Lawrence, as we have seen before, misunderstands Whitehead's earlier thoughts. All that is done in Principle of Relativity is a development of the doctrine found in Principles of Natural Knowledge and The Concept of Nature. From the totality of Whitehead's works, it is apparent that from the very beginning there was an element of "thought," "demarcation," "definiteness" in Whitehead's theory of perception.

NOTES

1. Whitehead now plainly rejects the kind of account of space, time, and motion which Russell had elaborated in The Principles of Mathematics.

2. PNK, p. 2.

3. PNK, p. 12. (Italics mine.)

4. PNK, p. 14.

5. PNK, p. 61. (Italics mine.)

6. PNK, pp. 111-112.

7. Robert Palter, Whitehead's Philosophy of Science (Chicago: The University of Chicago Press, 1960), p. 31.

8. CN, p. 197.

9. Lenzen mistakenly interpreted this second type of infinite event to be a duration. Cf. Chapter I of this paper.

10. PNK, p. 70. (Italics mine.)

11. CN, p. 105. (Italics mine.)

12. CN, p. 111. (Italics mine.)

13. PRel, N&G, p. 336. (Italics mine.)

14. For a further discussion of this matter see the section entitled "Palter" in Chapter V of this paper.

15. PNK, p. 71. (Italics mine.)

16. Apparently critics such as V. F. Lenzen and W. Hammerschmidt didn't realize that Whitehead himself was aware of this obstacle and addressed himself to it.

17. PNK, p. 74. (Italics mine.)

18. This interpretation is due to Schmidt who says that it is problem of any theory of perception to explain the transition from awareness to thought. This "indefiniteness of awareness leaves the door open for revisions in the fundamental concepts of science." P. 47. Whitehead remedies this "demarcation problem" in Process and Reality by introducing a new fundamental relation. See Chapter IV, "Revisions and Refinements."

19. Palter, p. 29.

20. CN, p. 144.

21. CN, p. 78

22. Nathaniel Lawrence, Whitehead's Philosophical Development (New York: Greenwood Press Publishers, 1968), p. 50. Hereafter this volume will be referred to by the author's surname only.

23. PNK, p. 81.

24. CN, p. 145. Lawrence bases this solution on Whitehead's own suggested use of his doctrine of significance in the case of an object (most likely an electrical particle) which manifests itself as a center of force in an electromagnetic field.

25. PNK, p. 167.

26. Rev. James Wright Felt, S.J., "Whitehead's Early Theory of Objects" (unpublished Ph.D. dissertation, Department of Philosophy, St. Louis University, 1965).

27. CN.P. 4. The text reads: Accordingly nature as disclosed in sense-perception is self-contained as against sense-awareness, in addition to being self-contained as against thought. I will also express this self-containedness of nature by saying that nature is closed to mind

28. CN, p.162. Schmidt rebukes L. Susan Stebbing for a position akin to Lawrence's. Stebbing seems reluctant to turn to Process and Reality for Whitehead's answer and wants a consistent view in the 1920 works. Schmidt feels that it is only with the theory of prehensions in Process and Reality that we get Whitehead's meaning of the "closure of nature to mind." Schmidt,p. 64.

29. W. Hammerschmidt in his book, Whitehead's Philosophy of Time, (New York: King's Crown Press, 1947), calls these "formal" and "non-formal" time. Lawrence says they are fundamentally the same.

30. Lawrence, p. 71.

31. PRel, N&G.

32. Ibid., pp. 307-08.

CHAPTER IV

THE METHOD OF EXTENSIVE ABSTRACTION

Purpose and Fundamental Notions of the Method

The method of extensive abstraction embodies Whitehead's attempt to derive systematically the fundamental "abstract" entities of natural science from factors given in sense-perception. As such it is the culmination, the climax of Whitehead's early philosophy of science.

Whitehead begins his deductive exposition by postulating the axioms for the fundamental properties of extension. The lists of these axioms differ slightly in PNK and CN. However, Whitehead meant the lists to be essentially equivalent with the exceptions of one minor correction in the later work. The list which follows is a conflation of the two lists: ("K" symbolizes "extension"; lower case letters signify events.)

i) aKb implies that a is distinct from b, i.e. part will always refer to the proper part. In other words, a is not part of itself. This makes K irreflexive.

ii) Every event extends over other events (and is itself extended over by other events). The set of events which an event e "extends over" is called the set of parts of "e." The phrase in parentheses is obviously redundant and is omitted later.

iii) K is transitive. If aKb and bKc then aKc.

iv) If aKc there are events such as b where aKb and bKc. This is the "density" property of K.

v) If a and b are any two finite events, there are events such as e where eKa and eKb. All events belong to a single manifold.(1)

99

vi) If the parts of b are also parts of a, and a and b are distinct then aKb. Two events are identical, therefore, when their respective sets of parts coincide.

Since the relation of extension is both irreflexive and transitive (Axioms i and iii), K is asymmetrical. The field of K is compact or has the property of density as was seen in Axiom iv. Axiom ii says there are no maximum or minimum events. Axioms ii, iv, and v together "postulate something like the existence of an ether," that is a continuum of events.(2)

Intersection, Separation, Junction

In an attempt to describe more adequately this continuum of events responsible for the continuity of nature, Whitehead defines the relationships of "junction" and "injunction." Intersection simply is the existence of parts common to two events and includes the case of one event extending over the other.(3) Two events are said to be separated if there does not exist any common parts.

The concept of the continuity of nature arises entirely from the relation called "junction" for which we find two alternative definitions.(4) These two logically independent definitions are the result of "direct observation" of the certain continuity inherent in the observed unity of an event.(5) Since the property of "extending over" includes by definition the property of intersection, the CN definition which utilizes the stronger requirement of "extension" is the stronger one. In fact, the PNK definition which requires only that there be an event "intersecting" both events is shown by Palter to be too weak to define junction in Whitehead's intended sense. The stronger definition is as follows:

Two events have junction when there is a third event of which both events are parts, and which is such that no part of it is separated from both of the two given events. Thus two events with junction make up exactly one event which is in a sense their sum.(6)

Junction of events includes two distinct cases--

100

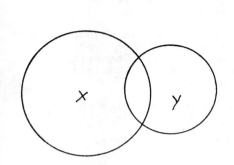

(i) Junction of intersecting events

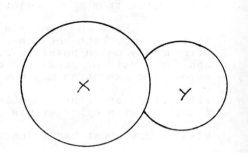

(ii) Junction of separated events
(or adjunction)

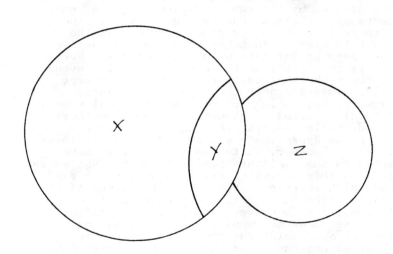

(iii) Injunction of events x and y (z is separated from x and adjoined to
y).

Fig. 4--Junction and injunction of events.(7)

101

injunction and adjunction. If the two events x and
y are both separated and joined they are said to have
adjunction. On the other hand, events x and y have
injunction when xKy and there is some third event
z separated from x and adjoined to y.

These two concepts of injunction and adjunction are important because they are the closest types
of boundary union possible for an event with its part
and for a pair of separated events. The two remaining
axioms for extension may now be stated:

vii) Every event has junction (and in particular adjunction) with other events.

viii) Every event has injunction with other events.

Abstractive Classes

The most vital concept in Whitehead's method
of extensive abstraction is that of an abstractive class
of events defined by the two conditions: (1) of any
two members of the class, one extends over the other,
and (2) there is no event extended over by all the
events in this class. In other words an abstractive
class possesses an infinite number of members. Very
important is the fact that there is no limiting event
to which the members of an abstractive set converge.
Abstractive classes appear to converge to points,
line-segments, etc. which do not represent real events
but are ideal entities of thought. As one considers
smaller and smaller events, the members of the abstractive class approximate closer and closer to these
ideal limits. However, Whitehead insists they never
do converge to any limiting, smallest event. But we can
correllate to this series of events quantitative expressions which represent them. The main issue of the
method is that the quantitative expressions of these
natural properties do converge to limits though the
abstractive set does not converge to any limiting
event.(8) We must point out the distinction here
between the events and their quantitative expressions.
Let e_1, e_2, e_3, ..., e_n, . . . represent the successive
members of an abstractive class. Let $q(e_1)$, $q(e_2)$, $q(e_3)$,
. . ., $q(e_n)$, . . . represent the set of quantitative
expressions which characterize the internal and external
relations of the successive events. Then the set of

102

events "s" converges to "nothing," but the set of
quantitative expressions q(s) converges to a class of
limits l(s). Whitehead now correlates another series
Q(s) of quantitative measurements to the series of
quantitative expressions q(s). If Q represents a particular quantitative measurement found in q(s), then
the homologous occurrences of Q throughout the members
of q(s) may converge to some definite limit. In summary:

> Thus the set s does indicate an ideal
> simplicity of natural relations, though this
> simplicity is not the character of any actual
> event in s. We can make an approximation to
> such a simplicity which, as estimated numeri-
> cally, is as close as we like by considering
> an event which is far enough down the
> series towards the small end. It will be
> noted that it is the infinite series, as it
> stretches away in unending succession towards
> the small end, which is of importance. The
> arbitrarily large event with which the series
> starts has no importance at all. We can
> arbitrarily exclude any set of events at the
> big end of an abstractive set without the
> loss of any important property to the set as
> thus modified. (9)

An abstractive set then begins with observable
finite events which constitute the "large end." By
means of an ordering relation (K) an indefinite number
of unobserved but theoretically observable events are
generated. The entire abstractive set approaches an
ideal limit "the ideal of a non-entity." This
ideal limit is not itself a concrete event in nature.
Palter believes that its ontological status, like other
mathematical entities can be satisfactorily discussed
only in Whitehead's later metaphysical works. Since
Lenzen found fault with the method on the grounds that
no quantitative series of empirical measure numbers--
essentially inexact--can ever approach an exact limit,
this interpretation of the status of an ideal limit as a
mathematical entity and not a concrete, observable event
is a vital one. Certainly, by a careful scrutiny of the
text it is a valid interpretation of Whitehead's thinking.
He takes care to state that the observed events never do
converge to a limiting event. Only by the mathematical
construction of correlated series of quantitative series

of expressions and measurements does one arrive at the
exact ideal limit.

"Covering" Relation

As in "La Theorie," abstractive sets converge
to different mathematical entities--chiefly points and
line-segments. Once again the property of "covering"
is utilized to gain precision in describing the convergence properties of abstractive sets.(10)

A class of events "a" is said to cover a class
of events "b" when every member of "a" extends over some
member of "b." Covering is non-symmetrical (neither
symmetrical nor asymmetrical), transitive, and reflexive.
If one abstractive set "a" covers another abstractive
set "b" and likewise "b" covers "a," the two sets are
equal in abstractive force. We say they are "K-equal."
K-equality is reflexive, symmetric, and transitive but
must involve infinite sets. The properties of primeness
and anti-primeness are now defined.

An abstractive class is said to be s-prime,
when for some given condition s:(11) (1) it satisfies
the condition s, and (2) it is covered by every other
abstractive class satisfying the condition s. On the
other hand, an abstractive class is s-antiprime, when
for some given condition s: (1) it satisfies the condition
s, and (2) it covers every other abstractive class satisfying the condition s.(12)

By definition any two s-primes must be K-equal
and any two s-antiprimes must be K-equal since they must
cover each other. Since an s-prime is covered by every
other abstractive class satisfying the condition s, an
s-prime has a "certain minimum of fullness among those
abstractive sets which are subject to the condition of
satisfying s." To put it simply, the convergence of
s-prime is the "sharpest" consistent with the condition
s. Contrariwise, "the intrinsic character of an
s-antiprime has a corresponding maximum of fullness."
Its convergence is the "broadest" possible consistent
with the condition s since it covers every other abstractive class satisfying the condition s.

In an attempt to single out those primes and
anti-primes which possess the sharpest and broadest

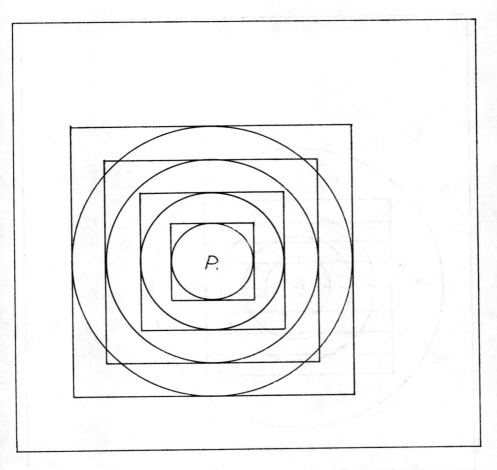

Fig. 5--Two K-equal abstractive classes, each "converging to
the "point" P. Notice the similarity between this
figure and figure 1.

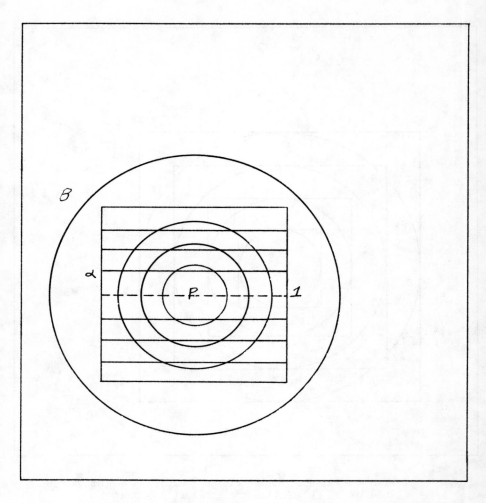

Fig.6--The covering of one abstractive class by another.
The set of circles B converges to the point P; the
set of rectangles ∝ converges to the line-
segment 1.   The abstractive class of events ∝
covers the abstractive class of events B, but not
conversely. (14)

106

convergence properties, Whitehead defines absolute primes and absolute antiprimes. There are inadequacies in both definitions, though Whitehead himself realized only that his definition of absolute prime required an important qualification. He did not admit, however, that his definition of absolute antiprime possessed the same deficiency.(13)

Abstractive Elements

In CN an abstractive element is defined as the "whole group of abstractive sets which are equal to any one of themselves." Whitehead's PNK definition employs the notions of primeness and anti-primeness.

Parallel to the theory of logical types, an abstractive element as defined in CN is one logical type higher than abstractive classes making it technically invalid to apply the relations of covering and K-equality. This disadvantage can be remedied according to a suggestion by Palter in which an abstractive element is redefined as the "class of events each of which belongs to at least one of the complete set of abstractive classes which are K-equal to one of themselves; that is, as the union of the members of the complete set of K-equal abstractive classes."(15)

Since finite abstractive elements will include space-time points (event-particles), and infinite abstractive elements will include "moments" their importance is undeniable. They enable one to deal simultaneously with all the abstractive classes of a given group of convergence-properties. Even following the PNK definition, an abstractive element "represents a set of equivalent routes of approximation guided by the condition that each route is to satisfy the condition s."

The Method and Time

Kinds of Space-time

In La Theorie, Whitehead distinguished four different meanings of the word "space." In PNK he gives three different meanings to the idea "space-time" in connection with external nature:

1) Four-dimensional space-time of which event-particles
are the points, and the point-tracks and null-tracks
are the straight lines. This space was introduced by
Minkowski and is the same for all observers.

2) Three-dimensional momentary (instantaneous) spaces.
Puncts are the points and rects are the straight lines.
The observed space of ordinary perception is an approxi-
mation to this exact concept.

3) The space of physical science, the time-less, three-
dimensional space of the time-system "a." Point-tracks
are the points, and matrices include the straight lines.

Instantaneous space and physical space are
relative to the observer's state of motion, and as a
result, are potentially infinite in number. Beginning
with a discussion of the exact concept of instantaneous
space to which the observed space of perception approximates, Whitehead advances first to define the fundamental
entities and relations in space-time, and then uses these
to define the fundamental entities and relations in
time-less space. The following is a useful schema of
Whiteheadian terminology.(16)

Geometrical Objects	Instantaneous Space	Space-time	Time-less Space
points (0-dimension)	punct	event-particle	point
straight lines (1-dimension)	rect	(point-track) (null-track) (set of co-rect event particles)	straight line
planes (2-dimension)	level	Matrix. Set of co-level event-parti-cles	plane

Moments are defined in terms of absolute anti-
primes and are then, in turn, used to define levels, rects,
and puncts. Event-particles, which are defined in terms
of absolute primes are, in turn, used to define other

space-time entities. The importance of primeness and anti-primeness is hence readily apparent.

Durations, Moments, Time-systems

We have already encountered Whitehead's notion of a duration as a finite slab of temporality. Since Whitehead himself was notably dissatisfied with his attempt at equating durations with members of absolute anti-primes, we will assume durations as a primitive concept posited by sense-awareness as factors in nature.(17) Influenced by the electro-magnetic theory of relativity, Whitehead also assumes a multiplicity of families of parallel durations. Parallel durations are pairs of durations extended over by some third duration, and all the durations parallel to a given duration inclusive form a _family_ of parallel durations, a concept familiar to mathematicians.

Moments, like durations, were first defined in terms of absolute anti-primes,(18) but in CN they are defined in terms of durations.

> It is convenient then to define a moment
> as the group of abstractive sets which
> are equal to some s-antiprime, where the
> condition s has this special meaning the
> property of being a class whose members
> are all durations. It will be found on
> consideration (i) that each abstractive
> set forming a moment is a s-antiprime,
> where s has this special meaning, and
> (ii) that we have excluded from member-
> ship of moments abstractive sets of
> durations which all have one common
> boundary, either the initial boundary
> or the final boundary.(19)

A family of parallel durations uniquely corresponds to a family of parallel moments, forming a "time-system." Four axioms are given to arrange the moments of a time-system serially.(20) Whitehead claims that "our sense-awareness of the passage of nature," provides the evidence for these axioms.(21) The fourth part of Axiom iv which asserts that "the serial order among moments of the same time-system has the Cantor-Dedekind type of continuity" has caused much criticism.

109

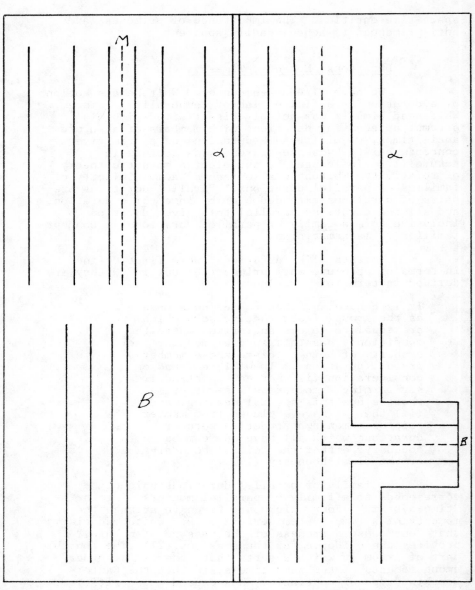

Fig. 7--Two abstractive classes
of durations, each
"converging" to the
moment M.

Fig. 8--Two infinite abstractive
classes: β covers α
but α does not cover β.

Palter, p. 58.

110

The problem posed by Whitehead's critics in this regard is how to reconcile a denumerably infinite class of primitive entities forming a family of durations and a non-denumerably infinite class of the moments of a time-system. A knowledge of the Dedekind cut may provide us with the answer.

A set is denumerable if it can be put into a one-to-one correspondence with the natural numbers. Examples of denumerable sets are the set of rational numbers and the set of algebraic numbers. A non-denumerable set is an infinite set which is not equipollent to the set of natural numbers, that is it cannot be put into such a one-to-one correspondence with the set of natural numbers. The set of real numbers and the set of irrational numbers are non-denumerable. Proof can be found in any text on Number Theory.(22) Sets that are equipollent to the set of real numbers are said to be of the power of the continuum. Dedekind, in his reconstruction of the theory of real numbers, introduced the definition of a "cut" which is intended to correspond to the naive conception of positive real numbers. A Dedekind cut is a set of rational numbers with the following three properties: (1) it contains some, but not all of the rational numbers, (2) every rational number belonging to the set is smaller than every rational number not belonging to it, and (3) it contains no greatest rational number. The cut is also called the "lower class" of the division of the number line, whereas its complement is called the "upper class."(23)

Indeed, the mathematician Whitehead, by mentioning the Cantor-Dedekind type of continuity explicitly did so for a purpose. If the non-denumerable infinite moments of a given time-system, impossible of detection through sense-perception, were thought of as subsets or "cuts" in the denumerably infinite class of moments which are, in principle at least, capable of detection in sense-perception, Whitehead can still claim that the method of extensive abstraction is based on sense-data. The Dedekind cut is a mathematical construct, a correspondence to the naive inexact conception of positive real numbers. Whitehead, in adopting it, gives more evidence that the method itself is similarly a mathematical construct corresponding to the world of sense experience.

111

Levels, Rects, Puncts

Moments from different time-systems may intersect. When two non-parallel moments intersect a level or instantaneous plane consisting of a set of abstractive elements and abstractive classes results. If a third moment should then intersect both moments in distinct levels, all three levels intersect in a common locus called a rect or instantaneous straight line. The three moments are then said to be "co-rect." If a fourth moment should then intersect the other three, a punct or instantaneous point arises. In PNK Whitehead asserts that the significance of a punct is that it "represents the ideal of the maximum simplicity of absolute position in the instantaneous space of a moment in which it lies." Definitions of parallelism of levels, rects, and puncts follow, and within any given moment the set of puncts, rects, and levels form a complete, three-dimensional, non-metrical, affine Euclidean geometry.(24)

The above derivation of levels, rects, and puncts from moments may explain Whitehead's remark that "all order in space is merely the expression of order in time." How else can we reconcile this statement with Whitehead's strong warning about the isolation of space and time found in CN:

> The explanation of nature which I urge as an alternative ideal to this accidental view of nature, is that nothing in nature could be what it is except as an ingredient in nature as it is. The whole which is present for discrimination is posited in sense-awareness as necessary for the discriminated parts. An isolated event is not an event, because every event is a factor in a larger whole and is significant of that whole. There can be no time apart from space; and no space apart from time; and no space and no time apart from the passage of the events of nature. The isolation of an entity in thought, when we think of it as a bare 'it,' has no counterpart in any corresponding isolation in nature. Such isolation is merely part of the procedure of intellectual knowledge.(25)

Event-Particles

An absolute prime can be defined as "an abstractive class which is prime with respect to the
condition σ, covering all the abstractive classes and
abstractive elements constituting some given punct."(26)
An event-particle is then defined as the finite abstractive element deduced from an absolute prime. If a
set of event-particles are all covered by a single
moment, they are said to be "co-momental." Two event-
particles are sequent if they are not co-momental.

We can analyze an event by the set of event-
particles inhering in it, in which case we say the event
"occupies" this set of event particles. An event can be
thought of as a locus of event-particles.

The Method and Space

Whitehead now turns his attention to space.
His first task to explain points in space by means of
abstractive elements converging to an absolute minimum.
Points arrived at in this fashion are ideal limits of
extensionless events. These ideal entities--the points
of instantaneous space, Whitehead admits do not
actually exist. He wants to push further and arrive at
the points of time-less space--the space of physical
science. These ideal minimum limits to events are
called (as we have seen) "event-particles." These can
be defined as abstractive elements, that is, groups of
abstractive sets. A point of time-less space, then, is
merely a class of event-particles.

Sufficiently small events of an event-particle
will either be parts of the event "e," or intersect or
overlap the event without belonging to it, or be
separated completely from the event. It is the second
case of intersection or overlapping which is of special
interest to us since these are the event-particles which
are said to bound "e." The complete set of event-
particles bounding an event constitutes the boundary of
"e."(28)

Event-particles or "instantaneous points" have
three aspects which recur in connection with all fundamental geometric entities: position in space, extrinsic
character, and intrinsic character. The Method concerns

113

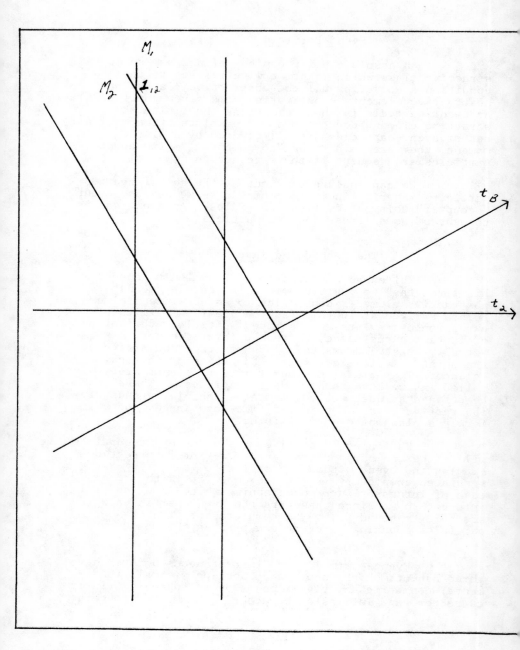

Fig. 9--Intersection in a level of moments from two time-systems. (27)

114

the first two of these:

> . . . consider a point of the instan-
> taneous space which we conceive as
> apparent to us in an almost instan-
> taneous glance. This point is an
> event-particle. It has two aspects.
> In one aspect it is there, where it
> is. This is its position in space.
> In another aspect it is got at by
> ignoring the circumambient space, and
> by concentrating attention on the
> smaller and smaller sets of events
> which approximate to it. This is its
> extrinsic character. Thus a point
> has three characters, namely its
> position in the whole instantaneous
> space, its extrinsic character, and
> its intrinsic character. The same
> is true of any other spatial
> element.(29)

We are now in a position with Whitehead to
substitute for the term "punct" the preferred "event-
particle." Levels and rects are merely loci of
event-particles--complete sets of event-particles
covered by appropriately intersecting moments.

Solids, Areas, and Routes

Though "solids," "areas," and "routes" can be
defined in a single uniform way by intersections of pairs
of spatio-temporal regions, each being one dimension
higher than the region to be defined, Whitehead gives
other definitions which are more suitable to a study of
specific types of spatio-temporal regions. Keeping in
mind (1) the knowledge that every geometric entity
possesses three distinct characters, and (2) the definition of a co-momental region as one covered by a single
moment, and finally (3) a vagrant region is one which is
not co-momental, we can follow Whitehead's exposition.

A solid is a set of event-particles common to
the boundaries of two adjoined events. If a solid is
co-momental or vagrant it is called a volume.(30) Co-
momental areas are loci of event-particles constituted by
the overlap (if any) of the two-dimensional boundaries of

115

a pair of volumes in a single moment. Again, relating
this back to our perception, Whitehead states:

> What we perceive as an approximation
> to our ideal of an area is a small
> event far enough down towards the
> small end of one of the equal ab-
> stractive sets which belongs to the
> area as an abstractive element.(31)

Overlapping areas whether co-momental or
vagrant are used to define routes (co-momental or vagrant).
In PNK and PR, however, Whitehead adopted another way of
defining routes as abstractive elements in which is found
the first advance (beyond event-particles) toward in-
creasing complexity. One of the most important types of
co-momental routes is the "straight" or "rectilinear"
route which is such that all the event-particles which it
covers lie on a single rect. Between any two event-
particles on a rect, obviously, there is exactly one
rectilinear route. In CN Whitehead calls rectilinear
routes "the segments of instantaneous straight lines
which are the ideals of exact perception." A kinematic
route is a type of vagrant route which represents a
possible path for a material object.

Cogredience

To complete his theory of straight lines in
space-time, Whitehead employs the relation of cogredience
to select a set of event-particles, one from each moment
of a single selected time-system. Points in time-less
space are the point-tracks of a parallel family. Point-
tracks are defined in complete analogy with the definition
of a moment, i.e. an infinite abstractive element, all of
whose members belong to abstractive classes composed
entirely of infinite events belonging to a single parallel
family--same time-system.

Points in time-less space are defined then as
the point-tracks of a parallel family. Intuitively, anything which occupies the point (set of event-particles)
is at rest within the given time system. Thus, there is
something akin to absolute position within each time-
system though motion and rest are relative to the time-
system:

116

Such a set of event-particles
will form a point in the timeless
space of that time-system. Thus a
point is really an absolute position
in the timeless space of a given
time-system.(32)

To finalize his Method, Whitehead defines new
entities called "matrices" to complete his theory of
planes in space-time. In any matrix there are two
families of parallel null-tracks, that is one member of
each family passing through each event-particle in the
matrix. Throughany given event-particle, then, there
is an infinity of null tracks which form three dimensional "conical" surfaces--their mutual vertex being
the given event-particle. Whitehead's rects, point-tracks,
and null-tracks correspond to straight lines in space-
time which are respectively space-like, time-like, and
null.(34) Since parallelism has been defined for all
three Whitehead has established an affine geometry for
space-time.

We have already seen that a point-track
(straight line of space-time) in its own time system is
a point in the timeless space corresponding to it. Likewise, if a set of parallel point-tracks in space-time lie
in a single matrix, this set defines a straight line in
that particular timeless space.

To complete his account for time-less spaces,
Whitehead finally defines two-dimensional flat spatial
entities. In CN a plane in the time-less space of a
time system "a" is the locus of all those points of the
space "a" which intersect any moment M of "a" in event-
particles lying on a single level in M.

We have now completed the non-metrical aspects
of the time-less, Euclidean, three-dimensional space of
theoretical physics. It is not until Process and Reality
that Whitehead attempts to derive the metrical aspects
of this space.

Congruence

Congruence is the theory of measurement in
space and time. Congruence, however, precedes the

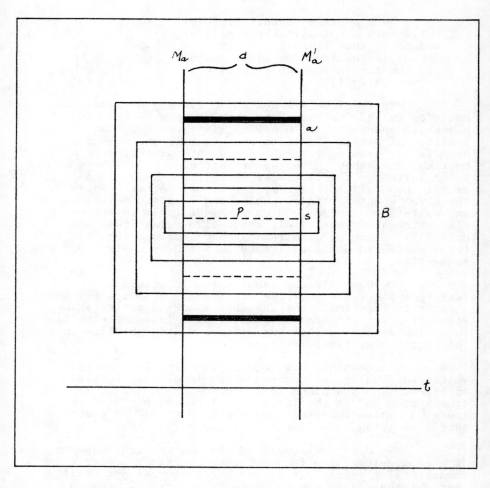

Fig. 10--The station s of the event-particle P in the duration
d bounded by moments M_a and M'_a (two dimensions of
M_a and M'_a are omitted). (33)

118

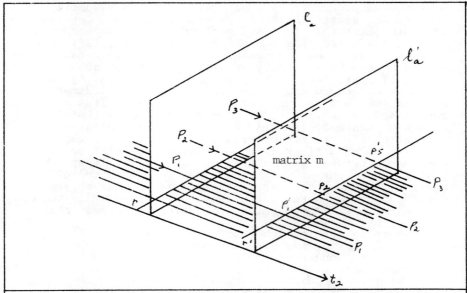

Fig. 11--Point-tracks and points; matrices and straight lines. Each point-track p_n defines a point in time-less space of t_a; the set of parallel point-tracks p_n in the matrix m defines a straight line in timeless space of t_a. (35)

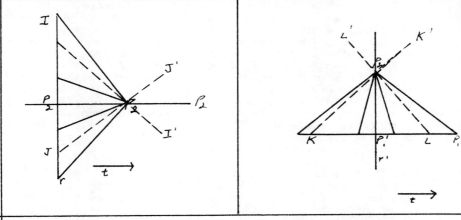

(i) The matrix m of Fig. 11 defined by P'_2 and r.

(ii) The matrix m of Fig. 11 defined by P'_2 and p_1.

Fig. 12--The relation between rects, point-tracks, and null-tracks within a given matrix. (36)

measurement procedure. If one were to use a yardstick to measure a distance it is of the essence of the operation of measurement that the yard measure remains unchanged as it is transferred from one position to another.(37) The judgment that we make concerning the unalterableness of the yard measure (if the yard stick is made of proper material) regardless of its successive positions is the judgment of congruence. Obviously, immediate judgments of this sort are presupposed in measurement. Thus we cannot define congruence by measurement. Henri Poincare, a French mathematician held that though several alternative axiomatic systems of relations of congruence can satisfy the conditions laid down which the relation of congruence between segments is to satisfy, it is an arbitrary convention which leads men to choose one of these alternate sets over another.(38) Man has chosen Euclidean over non-Euclidean geometry because it is more convenient. Whitehead interprets Poincare to mean that:

> There is nothing inherent in nature
> itself giving any peculiar role to one
> of these congruence relations, and
> that the choice of one particular
> relation is guided by the volitions of
> the mind at the other end of sense-
> awareness. The principle of guidance
> is intellectual convenience and not
> natural fact.(39)

Whitehead, of course, strongly disagrees with this position and recommends his theory as an explanation to the otherwise puzzling fact that mankind has agreed "in an arbitrary interpretation of sense-awareness where there is nothing in nature to guide it." According to Whitehead's theory there is in nature a factor "which issues in the preeminence of one congruence relation over the indefinite herd of other such relations."(40) Since space and time are now interconnected, a specific factor of time immediately distinguished in sense-awareness relates itself to one particular congruence relation in space. Congruence is a particular example of the fundamental fact of recognition.

It is not necessary for the thesis of this paper to examine in detail Whitehead's developments from observation and certain axioms of the congruence relations of rects and levels. It is of interest, however, to outline briefly the development of the congruence relations

120

as applied to lapses of time on non-parallel point-tracks. Whitehead's particular case of the axiom of kinetic symmetry upon which his method depends is that relative velocities are equal and opposite.(41)

By constructing a reference frame in time-system "a" by choosing four mutually normal axes (three for space, and one for time), an event-particle will have coordinates x_a, y_a, z_a, t_a. In another time system "b," the same event-particle will have the coordinates x_b, y_b, z_b, t_b. The two reference frames can be so arranged that their origin and two of the axes coincide. Transformation formulae for the a and b coordinates can then be found easily. These formulae contain several constants dependent on the a and b time-systems and the choice of time units in a and b. By then finding the relations between these constants, and expressions for the transformation of the components of the same velocity in system b, Whitehead is finally left with two constants-- one of which is expressible in terms of the other--and the velocity of system b in system a, that is of the velocity in system a of the point at rest in system b. Continuing on to the same velocity in a third time-system c, one constant remains which is expressible in terms of the relative velocity of the systems a and b and a certain invariant constant k for all time systems.

$$\frac{V^2_{ab}}{1-Q^{-2}_{ab}} = \frac{V^2_{gd}}{1-Q^{-2}_{gd}} = k$$

V_{ab} = velocity of system b in system a

Q_{ab} = constant for all transformations in system a, b.

V_{gd} = velocity of system d in system g.

Q_{gd} = constant for all transformations in that pair of systems.

By assigning different values to this universal constant, k, various kinematic results occur. If we allow k to be zero, results contrary to experience occur. If we assign k a positive value noting that since k evidently has the dimensions of the square of velocity and calling velocity c (putting c^2 for k) we get the well known factor of

121

relativity if c is identified with the velocity of
light.(42)

$$Q_{ab} = \left(1 - \frac{v_{ab}^2}{c^2}\right)^{-\frac{1}{2}}$$

By substituting the various constants of the
above transformation equations for an event-particle into
terms of Q_{ab} and substituting the above value of Q_{ab},
Whitehead arrives at the characteristic transformation
equations of the special theory of relativity.(43)

If we allow k to be negative, the resulting
type of kinematics has no distinction between time and
space "so that it would be natural to suppose that every
rect was a point-track and every point-track a rect.
. . . This does not appear to correspond to the properties
of the external world of events as we know it." Alto-
gether, there appear to be good reasons for putting aside
the elliptic type of kinematics as inapplicable to
nature.(44)

In the parabolic type of kinematics, we let
k = infinity and Q_{ab} = 1. This yields the formulae for
the ordinary Newtonian relativity which agree with common
sense and are suggested by ordinary experience but which
have been losing acceptance in the scientific world since
the Einstein theory appeared.(45)

The problem still remains as to what is the
value of k. It is not necessarily the speed of light
squared. The decision must be settled by an appeal to
experience far less general than the broad observational
basis which grounds Whitehead's philosophy. Yet, we know
the velocity must be extremely large--since with very few
exceptions due to extremely delicate apparatus, all our
experiences are satisfied by taking k = infinity. By
developing his formulae of relativity from the relation
of extension between events and axioms of congruence
relations of events, Whitehead's theory is not subject
to the defects of optical experiments--actual or ideal.
Whitehead has shown that man's experience of Nature,
even apart from those experiments upon which Einstein's
theory rests, lends no greater support to the supposition
of one space and one time than it does to a host of
theories of relativity distinguished by various finite

122

positive values of the constant k.(46)

Thus, Whitehead arrives at the transformation
equations of the special theory of relativity. He further
develops a law of gravitation. Though he acknowledges that
the general method of procedure is due to Einstein's great
discovery, his approach is quite different from Einstein's.
The final formulae of the two systems differ slightly
(agreeing in those instances where Einstein's results
have been verified.) What is remarkable about Whitehead's
theory is that though four-dimensional geometry is utilized, this geometry is Euclidean, not requiring the
curvature of the space-time manifold.

The Method as a Mathematical Model

We have just traced Whitehead's path from the
level of the sense perception of passing events to the
heights of mathematical relativity theory. The vehicle
he used to traverse this most difficult route was his
method of extensive abstraction. It is the central thesis
of this book that this method, acting as a "theoretical
bridge" between the perceptual and mathematical world, is
a genuine mathematical model. In order to defend this
thesis adequately we must begin with a survey of contemporary model theory. Then we will proceed to the
evaluation of Whitehad's method of extensive abstraction
in the light of such a survey.

Model Theory

With the progress of symbolic logic, modern
physics, and the social sciences, there has simultaneously
developed the theory of the scientific model. Max Black
distinguishes several types of models employed by scientists for various purposes. Scale models and analogue
models are symbolic but constructed devices used as
representations of some real or imaginary original.
Scale models are three-dimensional miniatures which include "all likenesses of material objects, systems, or
processes, whether real or imaginary, that preserve
relative proportions."(47) The analogue model is of more
interest to us since its making is guided by the abstract
aim of reproducing the structure of the original. They
ordinarily involve a change of medium. Famous examples

of analogue models are hydrolic models of economic
systems and the use of electric circuits in computers.

> An analogue model is some material
> object, system, or process designed
> to reproduce as faithfully as pos-
> sible in some new medium the
> structure or web of relationships
> in an original. . . . The analogue
> model, like the scale model, is a
> symbolic representation of some
> real or imaginary original, subject
> to rules of interpretation for
> making accurate inferences from the
> relevant features of the model.(48)

The dominating principle of the analogue model
is isomorphism; that is an analogue model will manifest
a one-to-one correspondence between the relations it
embodies and those embodied in the original. There must
be rules for translating the terminology applicable to
the model in such a way as to conserve truth value.

Because identity of structure allows a wide
variety of content, the possibilities for the construction
of analogue models are endless. There is a danger in this
however, for care must be taken that fallacious infer-
ences are not drawn from inevitable irrelevancies and
distortions in the model. Analogue models furnish
plausible hypotheses, not proofs.

Mathematical models

Another type of scientific model, similar to the
analogue model insofar as it represents an attempt to
reproduce structure, is the mathematical model. With the
rise of symbolic logic, the theory of such models has been
formulated. The standard definition given in most mathematical logic texts is one similar to Tarski's according
to which a model is a non-linguistic entity in which a
theory is satisfied.

> A possible realization in which all
> valid sentences of a theory T are
> satisfied is called a model of T.(49)

124

Suppes claims that Tarski's concept of model may be used
"without distortion and as a fundamental concept" in
many scientific disciplines--each discipline using the
concept differently. Mathematicians ask questions about
models which differ from those posed by empirical scientists. One question that all would most likely ask is
the technical meaning of "a possible realization" of a
theory. Suppes answers by saying, "Roughly speaking, a
possible realization of a theory is a set-theoretical
entity of the appropriate logical type." For example,
a possible realization of the theory of groups is any
ordered couple whose first member is a set and whose
second member is a binary operation on this set. This
formal definition of a model as a set-theoretical entity does not rule out the physical model--scale or
analogue--which is used by physicists. On the contrary,
the physical model may be simply taken to define the set
of objects in the set-theoretical model. The scheme
is as follows:

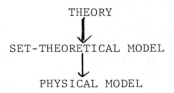

THEORY

SET-THEORETICAL MODEL

PHYSICAL MODEL

In classical particle mechanics, for example, the set-
theoretical model would be the axiomatized system which
would involve: (1) five primitive notions of a set P of
particles, (2) an interval T of real numbers corresponding
to elapsed time, (3) a position function (s) defined on
the Cartesian product of the set of particles and the time
interval, (4) a mass function (m) defined on the set of
particles, and (5) a force function (f) defined on the
Cartesian product of the set of particles, the time interval and the set of positive integers. The possible
realization of the theory of classical particle mechanics
is the ordered quintuple P = $\langle$P, T, s, m, f$\rangle$
A model of classical particle mechanics is any such
ordered quintuple. The actual physical model in the
physicists' sense is related to this set-theoretical
sense of models. We simply let the set of particles be
the set of planetary bodies (in the case of the solar
system). Suppes argues that it is the set-theoretical

125

usage of model which is more fundamental, although he
realizes that some empirical scientists would believe
that the physical model is more important to them.

Characteristics of a mathematical model

By "mathematical model," empirical scientists
usually mean the "mapping" of an "object system" upon
one or another of a number of mathematical systems or
models. In other words, the mathematics is there and
systematized (the theory of groups, quarternions, etc.)
and the scientist fits or forces his object system onto
the mathematics. This informal use of mathematical model
is often "no more than a pretentious substitute for
'theory' or 'mathematical treatment'," says Black who
suggests three additional characteristics of such a
model. First, the original field is conceived of as
"projected" upon the abstract domain of sets, functions,
etc. which constitute the subject matter of the correlated mathematical theory. Second, the model is
simpler and more abstract than the original. Finally,
the model is often suggested as a kind of ethereal
analogue model, i.e. the mathematical equations refer
to an invisible mechanism whose operation either illus-
trates or partially explains the operation of the
original system. This last suggestion is rejected as
being illusory.

In the use of a mathematical model several
procedures are involved. In the original field of investigation, a number of relevant variables are identified,
either on the basis of common sense or by reason of more
sophisticated theoretical considerations. (In Whitehead's
method of extensive abstraction, some of these variables
would be events, moments, and the like.) Empirical
hypotheses are framed concerning the imputed relations
between the selected variables. (One such relation in
Whitehead's method is the relation of extension over.)
Simplifications, often drastic, are then introduced for
the sake of facilitating mathematical formulation and
manipulation of the variables. (The introduction of
quantitative expressions which converge to a limit is
one such simplification Whitehead used for mathematical
convenience.) An effort is then made to solve the resulting mathematical equations--or failing that, to
study the global features of the mathematical systems

126

constructed. (Whitehead derived his theory of relativity and laws of gravitation from his method.) An effort is made to extrapolate to testable consequences in the original field, and by removing some of the initial restrictions imposed upon the component functions in the interest of simplicity lead to some increase in generality of the theory.(50)

The use of such procedures has many advantages flowing from the introduction of mathematical analysis into any domain of empirical investigation; namely, precision in formulating relations, ease of inference by means of mathematical calculation, and an intuitive grasp of the structures revealed. However some disadvantages also accompany the use of these procedures. Drastic simplifications made for the sake of mathematical analysis often result in confusing the accuracy of the mathematics with the strength of empirical verification in the original field. Mathematical treatment furnishes <u>no explanations</u>. Causal explanations must be sought elsewhere. (Whitehead only sought them during his metaphysical period.) It is this last characteristic that differentiates mathematical models from theoretical models.

Functions of scientific models

There is a diversity of functions fulfilled by mathematical models. Some models fulfill several aims; others, only one. Nine main functions underlying the utilization of scientific models are given by Leo Apostel as follows:

1) When no theory is known for a certain domain of facts, we replace our study of this domain by the study of another set of facts for which a theory is well-known and that has certain characteristics in common with the field under investigation. For example, in neurology we replace the central nervous system by a digital or analogue computer exhibiting certain of the neurological peculiarities.

2) For a domain of facts we have a full-fledged theory which is too difficult mathematically to yield solutions with our present technique. We then simplify assumptions to render the equations soluble.

3)   If two theories are without contact, we can use one as a model for the other or introduce a common model.

4)   If a theory is well confirmed but incomplete, we can assign a model in the hope of achieving completeness through the study of this model.

Special cases of this procedure are:

a)   a quantitative theory is known for a field but not securely established, and the model circumscribes the solid core of the theory in qualitative terms, and
(b) a qualitative theory is known for a field and the model introduces quantitative precision.

5)   If new information is obtained about a domain, we construct the earlier domain as a model of the later theory and show that all models of this theory are related to the initial domain.

6)   Models can be used to explain a theory about a set of facts, for instance, the particle or wave theories of light.

7)   Practical models can be constructed to represent a theory about an object too big, too small, too distant, too dangerous to be observed or experimented upon.

8)   We often need a theory present to our mind as a whole for practical or theoretical purposes. A model realizes this globalisation through either visualization or realisation of a closed formal structure.

9)   It often happens that the theoretical level is far away from the observational level; concepts cannot be immediately interpreted in terms of observations. Intermediary models are then introduced to constitute the bridge between the theoretical and observational levels. The theoretical as well as the observational predicates are interpreted as predicates of the model which furnishes lawful relationships between the two interpretations. This intermediary model can be used to construct the abstract theory or, once it exists, to find domains of application.(51)

          In summary, the functions of models may be theory formation, simplification, reduction, extension, adequation, explanation, concretisation, globalisation, action, or experimentation. Some models perform several of these functions simultaneously. The Method of Extensive Abstraction may be thought of as fulfilling, at least partially, the functions of quantitative completion (4b), globalisation (8), and serves as an intermediary between the theoretical level of science and the observational level of sense-perception (9).

Algebraic mathematical models

There are three types of classical and general models; the algebraic, the semantic, and the syntatical. Basically, algebraic models are isomorphisms. What is an isomorphism? Two sets D_1 and D_2 are isomorphic with respect to relations R and S defined respectively on D_1 and D_2 at least if: (1) there exists a mapping function F such that to each member of D_1 there corresponds one and only one member of D_2 under F, and (2) whenever members of D_1 stand in the relation R, their F-images stand in the relation S, and inversely. If these two conditions are satisfied we say that the two domains are isomorphic under the two relations R and S. Two sets will be completely isomorphic if they are isomorphic on all their domains.

Besides this general concept of isomorphism, several possible forms of approximation can be the case: The correspondence may be such that not always when R exists in D_1 between some elements, S exists in D_2 between the images of these elements. This relation can have an indetermination region for its domain and for its co-domain. Or, the correlator (mapping function) may be such that this function does not map the whole of the domain of R on S, nor the whole of domain S on R. We would then have an approximate direct or inverse correlator. Any combination of indetermination of domains, relations, and correspondence are considered as approximate isomorphisms. Naturally, the situation can become extremely complex, and we cannot hope to develop here a complete theory for these approximate concepts. It is noteworthy, though, that they are considered mathematical models. Apostel attempted to build a formal theory about approximate, partial, multiple, logically inconsistent, and vague models which do serve one or more of the above nine functions, but which do not satisfy the strict

129

requirements of isomorphism in the classical concept of
the model:

> We claim that we have made it plausible
> that a thorough analysis of the dif-
> ferent aims of model-building shows us
> that very definite structures are needed
> to achieve these aims, and moreover (and
> this is centrally important) (i) that
> these structures depart from the classi-
> cal concept of model in many different
> ways but (ii) that they can be studied
> and ordered, using this same classical
> concept of model as a centre of per-
> spective.(52)

Evaluating a model

Critics of the use of models in science claim
that the model is no more than a de facto contrivance for
leading scientists to a deductive system. Black disagrees with this view. Since the successful model must
be isomorphic with its domain of application, there is
a rational basis for using the model. Everything depends
upon the existence of a common structure in both fields.
If such a common structure exists, there is an objective
ground for the analogical transfer. The putative isomorphism between model and the field of application provides
the rationale for this particular mode of investigation
and yields standards by which we can critically judge
the model's value. We can determine the validity of a
given model by checking the extent of its isomorphism
with its intended application--determine the "goodness"
of its "fit."

Let us now examine Whitehead's method of extensive abstraction, and in the light of the above,
evaluate it as a mathematical (algebraic) model.

The Method as a Mathematical Model

A scientific model, mathematical or otherwise,
does not originate spontaneously in the human mind. The
senses must play an active part in the creation of any
model.

By means of the model we try
to grasp the essential facets of a
physical process; on the other hand,
the genesis of a model involves a
living contact with sensual observation. The model does not originate
spontaneously in the human mind,
but requires creative activity.
Thus senses and intellect both play
an active part in our shaping of the
model.(53)

We have already examined the theory of sense-
perception which forms the foundation of Whitehead's
method. As it appeared in the 1920 works, extensive
abstraction was no mere exercise in formal mathematics.
Whitehead's intention was to derive systematically from
empirical data and by means of mathematics the scientific concepts of modern physics. The theoretical level
of modern physics is far removed from the level of observation, and therefore a model is necessary to "bridge
the gap" (function 9 of Apostel). The Method also provided Whitehead with a desired globalisation through the
realization of the closed formal structure developed
therein (function 8).

The value of a mathematical model is directly
proportional to the similarity of structure existing
between the non-linguistic model and the theory at which
it is a possible realization. How did Whitehead set up
the correspondence or isomorphism required for the method
to be similar in structure to Nature?

The mapping function or correlator Whitehead
chose was that of correspondence or substitution. It is
often referred to as "equality," but the equality meant
is not one of identity but merely means "capable of being
substituted for." Whitehead consistently used the word
"is" instead of the more exact phrase "corresponds to"
when referring to the correspondence between mathematical
entities he correlated to the natural entities. For
example, we read in CN:

We now turn to space. The first
thing to do is to get hold of the
class of abstractive elements which

131

> are in some sense the points of
> space. Such an abstractive
> element must in some sense exhibit
> a convergence to an absolute mini-
> mum of intrinsic character. ......
> Thus an event-particle <u>is</u> an
> abstractive element and as such
> <u>is</u> a group of abstractive
> sets.(54)

Actually, to be technically correct, the passage should read "thus an event-particle <u>corresponds to</u> an abstractive element." In another instance, Whitehead writes, "Thus an abstractive element <u>is</u> effectively the entity meant when we consider an event-particle." This can be very misleading since Whitehead is safe in asserting that the abstractive element, corresponding to the event-particle, is an entity in nature; he cannot consistently assert, however, that the event-particle--the abstracted ideal limit--is such an entity. The event-particle is only potentially in nature. What Whitehead has attempted to do by the method of extensive abstraction is to put the logically constructed "event-particle" into a correspondence with an actual natural entity.

To continue, since a mathematical model applies only to elements which are defined by correspondence, to each geometric element such as point, instant, and the like used in extensive abstraction, there must correspond a natural entity. Whitehead aimed to satisfy this condition by defining geometric elements in terms of abstractive sets. Allowing the term "moment" to denote "nature at an instant"--an ideal--Whitehead defines "moment" in terms of durations and families of natural durations--both natural entities and perceptible. Abstractive sets of such durations are then constructed and their functions and properties are indicated. In like manner other mathematical entities employed in relativity are likewise defined.

Furthermore, in any model system, to any definite relation between the elements on one side there must correspond a definite relation between the corresponding elements on the other side. Only relations which have been so defined can be validly employed. Whitehead's defined relationships are parallelism, perpendicularity, cogredience and the like. True, many relations were left undefined, but this could be remedied easily. This is of no large concern. Our concern rests elsewhere; namely, with the condition that in an isomorphism the relations between entities and the entities themselves must be <u>necessary</u> <u>and</u> <u>unchangeable</u>.

Allowing a natural philosophy which would indicate that in nature there <u>are</u> indeed entities and relations which are capable of mathematical treatment precisely because these entities are exact and necessary per se, the method of extensive abstraction would be judged a general isomorphism since its necessary and exact structure would be analagous to the structure exhibited in Nature. On the other hand, if we accept the thesis that Whitehead's empiricism posits a Nature essentially lacking in necessity and exactitude, then the best we can say of the method is that it is an approximate isomorphism of the type described by Apostel.(55) The answer depends directly on the interpretation of Whitehead's empiricism and perceptual theory.

We will attempt an interpretation based on our previous analysis of Whitehead's early theory of perception. Since Whitehead suggests that the uniformity of the texture of experience "does not belong to the immediate relations of the crude data of experience but is the result of substituting for them more refined logical entities,"(56) the uniformity, regularity, and necessity ascribed to experience is provided by cogitation. In Whitehead's theory of perception we have indeed seen that there is an element of cogitation and thought which involves a logical construction, an instinctive inference. Sense-perception involves more than the immediately given. It contains hypothetical imaginative processes which provide aspects of perceptual objects not purely given. It is this cogitative element in perception which bestows natural entities and the relations of Nature with exactness--the exactness needed to set up the required isomorphism in the method of extensive abstraction. As we have noted previously, no event--natural entity--exhibits definite, spatio-temporal limits in perception, but through a continuous transition, demarcations are assigned to the event by an arbitrary

133

act of thought. It is a basal assumption essential for thought relating to perceptual experience that there are definite entities which are events.(57) Indeed, Whitehead assumed Nature to have definite entities and relations. O'Keefe did not admit this thought element as an integral part of Whitehead's empirical theory of perception, and therefore judged the method of extensive abstraction a failure:

> The reason why such an attempt is doomed to fail is this, that, no matter how we disguise the fact, the affirmations of mathematics are affirmations of exactitude and necessity. If we seriously make such affirmations about natural entities, we are affirming that there is exactitude and necessity in natural relations. Conversely, if natural entities are essentially inexact and involve no necessity, then these entities and their relations cannot be the object of exact and necessary mathematical statements. Exclude intellectual intuition of the exact and necessary in natural entities and you thereby destroy the rational foundation of applied mathematics.(58)

Whitehead did not exclude intellectual intuition of the exact and necessary in the process of perception. It would take another dissertation to examine whether Whitehead believed that there was a basis for this exactness in Nature. Personally, I believe that this was his fundamental belief. Nature is potentially exact and definite. The process of perception actualizes this potentiality. If therefore, we judge the method of extensive abstraction as an isomorphism between the mathematical entities and the natural entities as given in sense-perception, it is a classical algebraic model since it sets up a correspondence between natural perceived entities and geometric entities. If, however, we judge the method as an isomorphism between the mathematical entities and the natural entities per se (not as known through perception), then the best we can say is that the

134

method is an approximate isomorphism since it has not
been proved that these natural entities per se are
necessary and unchangeable. Neither has it been shown
that the relations of Nature are exact and work always
with no exceptions. However, even judging the method
in this way, it still can be given the label of a
"mathematical model." As such it furnishes no causal
explanations. These are sought later in PR.

According to Black's criteria for the evaluation of a mathematical model, everything depends upon
the extent of its isomorphism with its intended application.   As we have seen, Whitehead left much undone;
only several relationships and entities were defined
isomorphically. Therefore, the method cannot be judged
a "perfect fit." However, it is clearly a valid mathematical model as Wolfe Mays suggested. Furthermore, it
is grounded deliberately--and more or less successfully--
on an empirical base. As Victor Lowe asserted, it is an
empiracally well-based construction.

Refinements and Revisions

The problem of spatial extension had preoccupied
Whitehead as early as the Memoir of 1906. With his doctrine of events he succeeded in coherently integrating
the time factor with extension. As we have seen, events
are spatio-temporal--they possess temporal as well as
spatial extensiveness. In the 1920 books extensiveness
was synonymous with the extensiveness of events which
were Whitehead's ultimate entities replacing the Newtonian elements of space, time and matter.

In the period following PRel Whitehead came
to the realization that the relativistic theory of space
and time which he upheld posed a problem to his 1920
doctrine. If the ultimate characteristic of the actual
were spatio-temporal extension, does not this imply that
this extension is absolute and not relative? Ivor Leclerc
believes that it was this very consideration which
prompted Whitehead to delve into the ontological status
of extension.(59)

The term "extension" is not used in the cate-
goreal scheme of PR. The first mention of the term
only occurs in the succeeding chapter, "Some Derivative
Notions," where the extensive character of an actual

135

occasion, called its "region" is derived from its
character as an act of experience. William Christian
suggests two senses in which an actual occasion is
extensive.(60) First, an actual occasion is part of
the immediate experience of an occasion that is "here"
and "now." The "here-now" is its standpoint or region
or four-dimensional volume. It has thickness and
spread which are qualities of the occasion which also
has thickness and spread. The occasion takes time, is
stretched out spatially. Its region is a volume of
space through a duration of time. It is not divisible
into parts, but is a quantum of space-time. Temporally
it is not a moment but a duration--an epoch--a pause
in physical time. In a second sense, an actual
occasion as objectified for other actual occasions is,
in principle, indefinitely divisible. This divisibility
is what constitutes its extensiveness. When the satisfaction has completed the concrescence the occasion
becomes an object for succeeding occasions. It is an
objective fact or datum for analysis and abstraction.
The region associated with its satisfaction is now
spatially and temporally divisible. "The region is,
after all, divisible, although in the genetic growth it
is undivided." The region is now a potentiality for
division and subdivision by those actual occasions for
which it is an object. It is this indefinitely divisible
character of the given world which makes it an extensive
continuum.

Continuous extension, then, is not actually
real. Continuity is potential; actuality is atomic.

It cannot be too clearly understood
that some chief notions of European
thought were framed under the influence
of a misapprehension, only partially
corrected by the scientific progress of
last century. This mistake consists in
the confusion of mere potentiality
with actuality. Continuity concerns what
is potential; whereas actuality is in-
curably atomic.(61)

This recognition marks a radical change from the
philosophy of science works where events were both actual
existents as well as essentially continuous. The new
revision parallels Leibniz's conclusion that the onto-

logical status of extension as possibility must be that
of "ideality."(62) However, Leibniz went on to equate
this "ideality" with phenomenality, thereby opening the
door for Kant. Whitehead differs from Leibniz's view
that ideality must be relegated to phenomonality. Instead he utilizes the Aristotelain concept of "forms"
or "ideas" and makes these forms potentialities. He
calls these pure potentials, these possibilities for
actuality "eternal objects."(63) Potentiality is the
correlative of actuality for Whitehead, and is thus not
reducible to actuality. With this theory Whitehead's
relations are real relations and not merely rational
relations as Leibniz held. For Whitehead a relation
is real because it is a relating, an actualization of
form. Since patterns, structures, characters are all
forms, order is a real relatedness between actualities.
In this matter Whitehead differs from Descartes who
held that extension was real as well as actual:

> For Descartes the primary attribute
> of physical bodies is extension; for the
> philosophy of organism the primary re-
> lationship of physical occasions is
> extensive connection.(64)

Continuous extension in PR, therefore, is not a
basic feature of the actual events, but is a real relation.
Actual entities are atomic. Actuality is fundamentally
and metaphysically necessarily atomic. Extensiveness, on
the other hand, is a form of relatedness, a potentiality
for actualities. Leclerc states:

> It [extensiveness] is the most general
> scheme or structure exhibited by
> actualities whereby they stand in re-
> lationship to one another. It is the
> structure of potential standpoints.(65)

The potentiality of extensiveness is the extensive
continuum, which according to Whitehead is nothing but the
"potentiality for division; an actual entity effects this
division."(66) He goes on to explain that the extensive
continuum underlies the whole world, and "expresses the
solidarity of all possible standpoints throughout the
whole process of the world."(67) It is the first determination of order or real potentiality arising out of the
general character of the world.

137

Whitehead now derives space and time from extensive relatedness. In his earlier writings relations between events were inclusion, overlapping, and exclusion. In PR a theory of extension is not developed in terms of actual occasions but in terms of regions, the relata involved in the new relation of "extensive connection." This idea was introduced and suggested to Whitehead by T. de Laguna in "Point, Line, and Surface, as Sets of Solids." Laguna asserts:

> In the course of the development, a modified form of Professor Whitehead's method of "extensive abstraction" is introduced. The modification consists in the use, not of the relation of "extending over" (the relation of whole to part), but of the relation of "containing," in the sense of not simply including as a part but completely enveloping. Through this modification the method is greatly simplified and strengthened. It is, I believe, impossible by means of the method in its original form to give a definition of the point in terms of the solid.(68)

The two undefined concepts of "extensive connection" and "region" require an explanation. Christian suggests two meanings of "region." In the primary sense a region is the standpoint of an actual occasion. But in a more general sense the term is used "to include in its denotation spatio-temporal quanta which are not in fact standpoints of actual occasions, as well as quanta which are real standpoints." Some regions are merely hypothetical standpoints--they might be actualized by actual occasions.

> The divisions of the region are not divisions which are: they are divisions which might be. Each such mode of division yields 'extensive quanta': also an 'extensive quantum' has been termed a 'standpoint.'(69)

It is in this latter more general sense that the term is used in Process and Reality. Accordingly, not all

138

regions are regions of actual occasions.

Palter claims that this shift in the nature of
the ultimate entities of extensive abstraction flows
from the principle of Whitehead's philosophy of organism
which states that the internal and unextensive aspect of
an actual entity is an indivisible unity; the external
and extensive aspect of an actual entity is indefinitely
divisible.

Though Whitehead never says that his regions
are closed, he does state that "a certain determinate
boundedness is required for the notion of a region. . . .
The inside of a region, its volume, has a complete
boundedness denied to the extensive potential external
to it. The boundedness applies both to the spatial and
the temporal aspects of extension. Wherever there is
ambiguity as to the contrast of boundedness between inside and outside, there is no proper region.(70)

The possible connections among regions are
used to define the non-ordinal, non-metrical properties
of points, straight lines, and planes. Space and time
are not initially differentiated in the manifold of
regions and no specific type of region is presupposed.(71)
Two regions are extensively connected when they either
wholly or partly overlap or are in contact at a single
point or along parts of their boundaries.

Whitehead postulates the formal assumptions or
axioms required for extensive connection. The formal
properties of regions may be compared with those of events
for it is apparent that Whitehead intends the relata of
extensive connection (regions) to be formally almost
identical with the relata of extension (events).(72)
Furthermore, Whitehead and de Laguna tell us that the
relations of extension and inclusion are essentially
synonymous.

Palter points out the parallel between the sets
of axioms.

Axiom i--Definition (PR, p. 452)
Axiom ii--Assumption 9 (PR, p. 452)
Axiom iii--Assumption 6 (PR, p. 452)
Axiom iv--Non-abstractive Condition vii (PR, p. 463)
Axiom v--Non-abstractive Condition viii(PR. p. 463)

What interests us here is not the details of similarities. It is sufficient for our purpose to note that there are no important assumptions about regions which are not also true of events. The slight changes in the definitions of inclusion and overlapping are not essential. External connection is a redefinition of the concept formerly called adjunction. Tangential inclusion corresponds to injunction; overlapping corresponds to the junction of intersecting events. However, it is important to recognize that some of the extension axioms do not apply to all regions without exception. In accordance with the more general sense of the term "regions" Whitehead's non-abstractive conditions vii and viii refer only to members of a specific class or regions called an "ovate class" in the extensive continuum. (73)

Those assumptions which apply to all regions are those which define an abstractive class of regions, whereas the assumptions applying only to the ovate class of regions are the additional ones needed to define certain geometric entities such as straight lines which may be exemplified only in certain cosmic epochs. The only formal difference between regions and events mentioned by Whitehead is that regions are bounded—limited in extent, whereas events such as durations may be unbounded.

The method of extensive abstraction demands that its extended elements be indefinitely divisible. But in the later period individual occasions of experience are in no sense divisible into other occasions, but their respective regions are indefinitely divisible into other regions. Therefore, to meet the demand regions (not actual occasions) must be substituted for events. This necessitates the ontological categories implicit in the 1920 books become the explicit ontological categories of PR.

Since Whitehead has excluded unbounded regions (analogous to the earlier durations) from the ontological categories of PR, it becomes necessary in the new formulation of extensive abstraction to define points without durations. Whitehead thus replaces the relation of extension by that of extensive connection.

In the 1920 works the whole-part relation was a

140

primitive concept. Palter believes this choice subtly emphasized the notion of subdivision over that of aggregation. In PR the relation of extensive connection subtly emphasizes connections between wholes rather than parts of wholes. This choice gives the method a marked gain in generality since "the somewhat more general notion of 'extensive connection' can be adopted as the starting point for the investigation of extension: and . . . the more limited notion of 'whole and part' can be defined in terms of it." Basic geometric entities can now be defined independently of moments (and therefore of durations). It is of value to quote Whitehead at this point:

> If we confine our attention to the
> subdivision of an actual entity into
> coordinate parts, we shall conceive
> of extensiveness as purely derived
> from the notion of 'whole and part,'
> that is to say, 'extensive whole and
> extensive part.' This was the view
> taken in by [sic] my two earlier
> investigations of the subject
> [PNK and CN]. This defect of starting
> point revenged itself in the fact that
> the 'method of extensive abstraction'
> developed in those works was unable
> to define a 'point' without the
> intervention of the theory of
> 'duration.' Thus what should have
> been a property of 'durations' became
> the definition of a point. By this
> mode of approach the extensive re-
> lations of actual entities mutually
> external to each other were pushed into
> the background; though they are equally
> fundamental.(74)

Palter interprets this passage as nothing more serious than Whitehead's admission of an "inappropriate logical arrangement of definitions, in which durations are used to define points (and also flat geometrical entities) instead of being defined by them." The passage does not represent a repudiation of the concepts defined in the earlier formulation of the method. In the generalized method of extensive abstraction (minus durations as primitive entities), Whitehead's purpose,

141

according to Palter, seems to be to base the method on
extensional data prehensible in principle at least by
any actual occasion in any cosmic epoch. In PNK and CN
where Whitehead utilized durations to derive the four-
dimensional space-time manifold of the present cosmic
epoch, such a use is deemed legitimate and even necessary.

It is not the purpose of this paper to analyze
the generalized method of extensive abstraction.(75)
It is sufficient to note as we have the major revisions
and their purposes. What is of importance to us is the
recognition that Whitehead does not reject his earlier,
more restricted formulation of the method developed in
PNK and CN. These earlier works were concerned with his
philosophy of science and were restricted to the space-
time manifold of our present cosmic epoch. As such they
are grounded on sense-perception. In PR Whitehead's
major concern is metaphysical and ontological. Metaphysics is now seen as indispensable to any philosophy
to any philosophy of science. This shift to metaphysics
involved a new set of problems, different from those
which had previously been his concern. Leclerc comments:

> This involved also a change to a
> different method or procedure from
> that which he had previously adopted.
> His earlier endeavor had been to
> provide a set of concepts as a
> foundation for natural science.
> This concern with the foundational
> concepts of science he conceived as
> constituting the "philosophy of
> science." Whitehead thought of it. . .
> as an enterprise with limited ends
> which it was possible to pursue by
> the essential scientific method, and
> in particular in abstraction from
> metaphysical considerations as to the
> nature of things in themselves.(76)

The shift to metaphysics does not constitute an
abandonment of his earlier problem. Whitehead had merely
come to see that indispensable to the philosophy of
science is an elucidation of concrete fact from which
the sciences abstract. This is the task of metaphysics.

Whitehead's elaboration of the method in PR suffers a loss of its empirical base and reappears as a more formally mathematical deduction. It is not disjunctive from the philosophy of science works, but is a metaphysical approach to the problem which we saw Whitehead tackling mathematically in the Memoir of 1906 and epistemologically in PNK and CN. In its new metaphysical dress, the method may still be regarded as a mathematical model, but it is one which is more abstract with metaphysical overtones.

NOTES

1. Axiom ii can be deduced from this.

2. PNK, p. 102

3. Ibid.

4. PNK, p. 102; CN, p. 76.

5. CN, pp. 76-77.

6. CN, p. 76.

7. Palter, p. 48.

8. CN, p. 61.

9. CN, pp. 81-82.

10. See page 84, Chapter II of this paper.

11. The Roman letter "s" is being used instead of the Greek sigma for typographical reasons.

12. Because different definitions of primes and antiprimes are given in CN and PR, we are following Palter's interpretation.

13. For the inadequacies in both definitions, see Palter, pp. 53, 63.

14. Palter, p. 51.

15. Palter, p. 53.

16. This schema is based on Palter's, p. 55.

17. See his notes in CN, pp. 197-98; PNK, p. 204.

18. PNK, p. 110

19. CN, p. 88. Palter casts doubts as to the existence of the type of absolute antiprimes identified with s-antiprimes used to define moments. He bases his doubts on his own illustration of two infinite abstractive classes where b covers a, but a does not cover b. Since moments can be defined independently of absolute anti-primes, this problem of their existence is not major. However, assuming the existence of absolute antiprimes, we must exclude abstractive classes of durations with a common boundary--a feature lacking to absolute primes. See Palter, pp. 58-59.

20. PNK, pp. 114-15.

21. CN, p. 63.

22. Alexander Abian, The Theory of Sets and Transfinite Arithmetic. (Philadelphia and London: W. B. Saunders Co., 1965), chapters v and vi.

23. S. Korner, The Philosophy of Mathematics (New York: Harper and Row, Publishers, 1960), p. 189.

24. In affine geometry, parallelism but not congruence occurs.

25. CN, pp. 141-42. (Italics mine.)

26. Palter, p. 63. Palter notes that Whitehead qualifies this definition by eliminating from consideration some exceptional cases he discovered.

27. Palter, p. 60.

28. "An event-particle bounds an event "e" when every event in which the event-particle inheres intersects both "e" and events separated from "e." Palter, p. 64.

144

29. CN, pp. 89-90.

30. A volume may also be defined as the set of event-particles in which a moment intersects an event, provided the set is not empty.

31. CN, p. 103

32. CN, pp. 105-06.

33. Palter, p. 70.

34. Palter, p. 75.

35. Palter, p. 72.

36. Ibid., p. 74.

37. CN, p. 120.

38. Henri Poincare, Science and Hypothesis (New York: Dover Publications, 1952) p. 50.

39. CN, p. 122.

40. CN, p. 124.

41. E. V. Miller, "The Emergence of Relativity in Alfred North Whitehead's Philosophy," Australian Journal of Psychology and Philosophy, Vol. I (1923) pp. 256-67.

42. Palter, p. 83.

43. PNK, p. 159.

44. When k is positive we have hyperbolic kinematics; when k is negative, elliptic kinematics; when k is equal to infinity, parabolic kinematics. There is no connection between these kinematics and hyperbolic, elliptic, and parabolic geometrics.

45. PNK, p. 163; CN, p. 131.

46. Miller, p. 266.

47.   Max Black, <u>Models and Metaphors</u> (Ithaca, New York: Cornell University Press, 1962), p. 220.

48.   <u>Ibid</u>., p. 222.

49.   As cited by Suppes, p. 163.

50.   Black, pp. 223-25.

51.   Leo Apostel, "Toward the Formal Study of Models in the Non-Formal Sciences," <u>Model in Mathematics</u>, pp. 1-3.

52.   Apostel, p. 16.   (Italics mine.)

53.   A. Kuipers, "Model and Insight," <u>Model In Mathematics</u>, p. 132.

54.   CN, pp. 85-86.   (Italics mine.)

55.   This is the thesis put forward by Thomas O'Keefe in "Empiricism and Applied Mathematics in the Natural Philosophy of Whitehead," <u>Modern Schoolman</u>, Vol. XXVIII (1950-51), pp. 267-89.

56.   STR, AE, p. 163.

57.   See Chapter III, pp. 108-109.

58.   O'Keefe, p. 288.

59.   Ivor Leclerc, "Whitehead and the Problem of Extension," <u>The Journal of Philosophy</u>, Vol. LVIII (1961), pp. 559-565.   Our page references will be from the reprint of this article in Klein's volume, previously cited.

60.   William A. Christian, <u>An Interpretation of Whitehead's Metaphysics</u> (New Haven: Yale University Press, 1959), pp. 80-82.

61.   PR, p. 95.

62.   Leclerc, <u>Klein</u>, p. 120.

63.   PR, p. 32.

64. PR, p. 441.

65. Leclerc, p. 122.

66. PR, p. 104.

67. PR, p. 103.

68. T. de Laguna, "Point, Line, and Surface, as Sets of Solids," The Journal of Philosophy, Vol. XIX, No. 17 (1922) p. 451.

69. PR, p. 435.

70. PR Corrigenda, p. 544.

71. Palter, p. 106.

72. Palter, p. 109.

73. Palter believes that Whitehead had in mind "convexity" when he adopted the term "ovate." Palter, p. 120.

74. PR, pp. 439-40.

75. See Palter, pp. 106-46 for such a detailed development.

76. Ivor Leclerc, "Whitehead's Philosophy," Review of Metaphysics, Vol. XI (1957), p. 88.

CHAPTER V

A BACKWARD GLANCE

This study was designed to resolve the current
debates concerning the success or failure of Whitehead's
method of extensive abstraction by (1) tracing the
origin and subsequent development of Whitehead's method
from the memoir "On Mathematical Concepts of the
Material World" (1905) to the revisions made in
Process and Reality (1929), (2) showing that the
process of perception, containing as it does an element
of cogitation, endows natural entities with definiteness
and exactness, and (3) indicating that the method is a
mathematical model according to the norms of contemporary
model theory. As such a model the principle of extensive
abstraction validly employs mathematical simplifications,
conveniences, and techniques. Our findings in connection with each of these points will now be reviewed.

Evolution of the Method

The Memoir of 1905

The method of extensive abstraction is a
mathematical construct devised by Whitehead to define
the simple concepts of space and time such as "points,"
"lines," and "instants" in terms of relationships
observed in the perceptual flux. The technical beginnings
of the method were traced as far back as the Memoir of
1905 where the theories of interpoints and dimensions
were formulated in order to remove the circularity inherent in the definition of a point as a class of straight
lines concurrent at a point. In the Theory of Interpoints, Whitehead includes temporal entities in the point-
defining relation and introduces the notion of "cogredience." In the Theory of Dimensions, based on a new

149

definition of the dimensions of space, Whitehead contributes to the theory of classes and applies the latter theory to geometry.

The dominant theme which runs as a strand through all of Whitehead's transitional philosophy of nature is his dissatisfaction and criticism of the Newtonian Classical World Concept. At first (1905) Whitehead finds fault with this world-view on the grounds that by positing three primitive entities--points of space, instants of time, and particles of matter-- the Concept violates the Principle of Economy. However, by 1920 Whitehead's main reason for rejecting the Newtonian Concept is its lack of agreement with observed nature.

In the Memoir of 1905, Whitehead offers as alternatives to Newton's world model two _linear_ world concepts which have hypothetical linear reals as their basic elements. Spatial points are derived from these linear reals in a manner similar to the method employed in projective geometry. A point is a bundle of linear reals concurrent at a point; it is made up of a converging series of lines.

La Théorie Relationniste de l'Espace

In his 1914 address a Congress of logicians in Paris, Whitehead develops a more sophisticated derivation of points from a converging series of overlapping volumes. It is this latter definition of points which Whitehead employs in the method of extensive abstraction. By this time Whitehead has not only accepted the relational theory of space but has already begun translating it into the language of symbolic logic. The word "space" has four distinct meanings: (1) immediate apparent space or the here-now limited space of an individual perceiver, (2) complete apparent space or the mental completion of the totality of all the individually perceived immediate apparent spaces, (3) physical space which is the space of science and is the same for everyone, and (4) abstract space, the space of formal geometry. Whitehead develops the relational theory of space for both complete apparent space and physical space. Perceived objects in apparent space are related to a complex of relations among physical objects in scientific space. This relationship or

parallelism is asserted to be the only essential
characteristic of the physical world of science. In
other words, Whitehead believes that the structure
exhibited in apparent space corresponds, in some way,
to the structure manifested in scientific space. The
nature of this structural correspondence is the subject
of the three 1920 books. Progress in science can be
made only by substituting exact, definite, more permanent scientific entities for the unstable objects of
apparent space. Furthermore, any exact science in
order to be of value must provide for an approximative
interpretation of its exact theorems. Whitehead illus-
trates what he means by this by defining a point in
physical space as an area or volume sufficiently small
not to allow a useful division. This is an approximative
usage of the exact mathematical concept of a point.

        For mathematical convenience, and for this
reason only, Whitehead adopts the hypothesis of infinite
divisibility which is the foundation of the continuity
of space. He readily admits that this hypothesis
cannot be proved, and that, indeed, the existence of
minima visibilia in apparent space seems to contradict
it. Whitehead also employs the mathematical principle
of convergence to a conceptual limit in the derivation
of points recognizing that the principle does not simply
apply. Precise meaning of convergence of overlapping
volumes could only be had by a special hypothesis.
Whitehead has been criticized harshly for the use of
thewe two mathematical techniques (infinite divisibility
hypothesis and the principle of convergence to a limit)
in the method of extensive abstraction. In fact most
of the charges made in the "three debates" involve, in
some way or another, these very principles. His rejoinder
to the charges would, I believe, be similar to the reasoning he expressed in the 1914 address. He used these
principles for mathematical convenience and simplicity
fully realizing that he was utilizing them in an approximative manner. Any exact science must allow for this.

Theory of perception of events

        The Principles of Natural Knowledge (1919)
begins with a familiar theme--the critique of the
Newtonian Classical Concept with its three fundamental
entities--points, instants, and unextended particles.

Whitehead does not deny that such entities are useful
or even indispensable. His problem is the status of
such elements as ultimate constituents of nature.
The Classical Concept does not seem to agree with the
observable state of nature. Yet, physics cannot get
along without Newton's points, instants, and matter.
Whitehead sets as his goal the definition of entities
which would have the same formal properties and do the
same work as Newton's points, instants, etc. but which
would also be connected with the objects that we do perceive and with their perceptible relations. Whitehead
wanted entities which would be certain logical functions
of what we perceive--functions of logically higher types
than the type of particular existents to which they are
related.

        Whitehead's purpose, then, is to start with
genuine perceivable elements of nature and their relations as definite logical functions of the former.
Whitehead's theory of perception determines what these
natural elements are: the method of extensive abstraction is the detailed exhibition of the concepts as
functions of them.

Events

        Nature consists of two fundamentally different
but intimately connected types of entities--events and
objects. Events are the ultimate facts; they are
happenings or facts in the becomingness of nature.
Objects, on the other hand, are characteristics of
events which are, in turn, the situations of objects.
Objects are ingredient in events. Events cannot recur
in time or space but objects can insofar as different
events can be the situations of the same object. Events
are introduced to avoid the bifurcation of nature into
two distinct types of realities--nature apprehended in
awareness and nature which is the unperceived cause of
the awareness. In a way events replace the traditional
notion of "substance," but their properties are quite
different. The subject-predicate logic and substance-
attribute metaphysics are condemned by Whitehead as
instances of the fallacy of misplaced concreteness
(mistaking the abstract for the concrete).

        Events may be durations or parts of durations.
Durations are the whole course of nature contemporary

with the spacious present of any percipient; they are limited temporally but unlimited spatially. In any duration the events connected with the mind and bodily life of the percipient occupy a unique position, the "here-now" in the duration. This event is called the percipient event and it is related to its duration by the property of cogredience. Cogredience not only makes possible unequivocal meanings to the experienced "here and now," but it is also fundamental to the relation of absolute position and the derivative ideas of motion and rest.

An event has many characteristics; six of these, the constants of externality, answer the basic questions, "Which?" "What?" "How?" "When?" "Where?" and "Whither." Because events appear as indefinite entities without clear demarcations there must be a continuous transition by which definiteness and exactness are assigned to them by an arbitrary act of "thought." This "cogitative" act corresponds to no perceptual experience but is a basic assumption essential for reasoning. The first awareness of events is blurred and vague; it requires "thought" to achieve definiteness. Whitehead's meaning for "thought" is rather a unique one; it in no way means ratiocination. It is rather a "bestowing of definiteness."

There are a great many ways that the diversification of nature can be analysed. Some modes of analysis are more useful than others. One very useful method leads to events which are situations of sense objects, perceptual objects, physical objects, and scientific objects alike. Objects are ingredients of events which make possible the comparison of events and their demarcation. Perception involves, as we have noted, the recognition of objects. Objects are classified by Whitehead in verious ways. A very broad division is between uniform objects which require no minimum of time-lapse in the situation, and non-uniform objects which demand such a time span. If one were to diminish repeatedly the time span of a non-uniform object such as a tune, one destroys the tune.

Scientific objects are the most problematic of the Whiteheadian objects. Whitehead speaks of them in two different senses--what Felt has termed the "denoted sense" and the "denotive sense." In the denoted sense they are within nature and refer to causal

153

characteristics of events. In the denotive sense they
are within the mind and refer to our imperfect mental
conceptions of these causal conditions. It is our view
that Whitehead meant that scientific objects are in
nature as the ground for the more exact, abstract conceptions present in the mind through intellectual
inference.

Revisions and refinements were made in Whitehead's theory of perception during the later years of
his philosophy of nature period as part of his attempt
to reconcile his early sensationalistic point of view
with his parallel tendency to argue for a realistic
theory of knowledge. Perception in 1924 contains more
than awareness; it contains thought. Cogitation--
consciousness of factors abstracted from their background of fact--is a refinement and further limitation
of awareness which is merely a crude type of consciousness.

Whitehead's view of perception has been shown
in Chapter III to provide a foundation for the philosophy of science formulated in the 1920 books. From the
notions of events and their internal relations, a
relational theory of space-time can be derived. The
status and functions of scientific objects are explained.
But, while the theory of events and objects was intended
as a means to avoid the bifurcation of nature, Whitehead
has established a bifurcation of his own, so to speak,
in his dualistic distinction between events and objects;
events accounting for the continuity and passage of
nature, and objects for atomicity.

The method of extensive abstraction

The fundamental relation among events is that
of "extending over" one another. Events endure and
overlap. As a fragment of the specious present, an
event has both spatial and temporal extension. A pair
of such fragments may be related in such a way that one
spatio- temporally covers the other and extends beyond
it. This is what Whitehead meant by "extending over."
The relation of extending over is asymmetrical, transitive, and has a compact field. Yet, the relation is not
a serial one since, although all events extend over
some events and are extended over by others, there are
pairs of events which do not have either of these

relationships to each other.

The most important concept of extensive abstraction is that of an abstractive class of events. An abstractive class of events is a series of events extending over each other like Chinese boxes but with no smallest box. Technically, an abstractive class of events is defined by the two conditions: (1) of any two members of the class, one extends over the other, and (2) there is no event extended over by all the events in this class. Abstractive classes approximate closer and closer to an ideal limit without ever coverging to it. Therefore, correlated to this converging series of events is a series of quantitative expressions and another series of quantitative measurements which do indeed converge to definite limits.

Abstractive sets converge to various geometric entities such as points, lines, etc. The covering relation describes precisely the convergence properties of abstractive sets. The concepts of primeness and antiprimeness are introduced to facilitate the definitions of the fundamental geometric entities. An abstract class is prime with respect to any formative condition "s" when (1) it itself possesses the property "s," and (2) it is covered by any abstractive class that also possesses the property "s." A prime is a sort of minimum abstractive class out of all those with a given property. In contrast, an antiprime is a sort of maximum abstractive class. Antiprimeness can lead to moments by way of durations since a moment refers to a whole of nature spread out in space. Primeness leads to event-particles, which are events thought of as unextended in space and time.

To define moments and event particles, a restriction must be placed on the formative condition of abstractive classes. The restriction is that the property "s" shall be regular for primes and antiprimes, "s" is regular for primes when (1) there are abstractive classes which are prime with respect to "s, and (2) all such classes cover and are covered by each other. Such classes are said to be "K-equal."

An absolute antiprime is a class that covers every class that covers it. It is a sort of absolute maximum among abstractive classes. Any member of any such absolute antiprime is what we mean by a duration.

Since Whitehead was dissatisfied with this above attempt at defining a duration in terms of antiprimes, he later assumed durations as primitive entities without any losses--indeed even with some gain--to the method of extensive abstraction.

Moments, like durations, were first defined in terms of absolute antiprimes, but are then redefined in The Concept of Nature in terms of durations. Abstractive elements are also defined in The Principles of Natural Knowledge, the earlier work, in terms of primeness and anti-primeness, but are redefined in The Concept of Nature as the "whole group of abstractive sets which are equal to any one of themselves."

We can now proceed to a definition of parallelism of durations and moments. If there be a single time-series independent of change of spatial axes, as the Newtonian Classical theory holds, any pair of durations will be extended over by some third duration. But, according to Einstein's theory of relativity, the temporal coordinates have to be varied as well as the spatial ones on passing from one set of axes to another in relative motion. In this case, durations of two different time series are not extended over by some third. Only durations of the same time series fulfill this condition. Whitehead thus defines durations as parallel when any pair are extended over by a third; in other cases they are not parallel. Moments corresponding to a set of parallel durations are parallel moments. Families of parallel durations and their moments constitute time-systems.

When a pair of non-parallel moments intersect, an instantaneous plane or "level" in the time-system of either moment results. Levels are parallel if they are the intersections of a moment by two moments of another time-system; otherwise levels intersect. Their intersections are called rects which are instantaneous straight lines. Finally, two rects may intersect resulting in a punct--a point of instantaneous space--in the spaces of the moments in which it lies. Puncts, rects, and levels form an instantaneous Euclidean space in a moment of a given time system. This instantaneous space is the space to which our perception of space approximates.

To define event-particles we must break out of

156

the restriction to single moments in single time-systems. Event-particles are connected with absolute primes in much the same way as moments are connected with absolute anti-primes. All the event-particles in the whole course of nature form the points of a four-dimensional space-time manifold. Any finite event can, in a way, be analysed into the set of event-particles that inhere in it. No event-particle is a part of an event in a physical sense since it is an object of an entirely different logical type. But there is a unique correlation between any event and a certain bounded set of event-particles which form a continuum. If one event be a physical part of another, by isomorphism the set of event-particles correlated with the former will be a logical part of the set correlated with the latter.

Thus far, two types of space with their characteristic geometries have been considered: (1) the three-dimensional Euclidean space of a given instant in a given time-system. Our perceived space is an approximation of this type of space which has puncts, rects, and levels as its points, straight lines, and planes. (2) the four-dimensional "space-time" which is neither space nor time but a compound of both whose points are event-particles. Whitehead treats a third type of space called a "timeless" space which unlike Euclidean space is neutral as between all the moments of the time-system to which it belongs.

For the purpose of deriving a geometry for this last type of space which is the space of physics, the undefinable relation of cogredience is introduced. Abstractive classes of cogredient events are used to define a station which is an ideal limit of a set of cogredient events covering an event-particle as these events get spatially thinner and thinner. A station intersects every moment in its duration in a single event-particle. Any station in a duration of a time-system can be prolonged throughout all the durations of that system. The set of event-particles on such a prolonged station is called a "point-track." Point-tracks play a dual role. They are the straight lines joining pairs of sequent event-particles in the four-dimensional space-time, and they are the points of the timeless space associated with our own time system. The straight lines of space-time are completed by the addition of "null-tracks" and sets of "co-rect event-particles" which are correlated with the rects of three-dimensional space.

Lastly, the planes of space-time are completed by "comomental planes" (which are correlated with the levels of three-dimensional geometry) and matrices which include both comomental and non-comomental planes.

The elements of the geometry of four-dimensional Minkowskian space-time are now completed. However, it still remains to define the straight lines and planes of time-less space of a given time system. This is not difficult to do since a point-track in its own time-system is a point in the timeless space corresponding to it. Likewise, if a set of parallel point-tracks in space-time lies in a single matrix this set constitutes a straight line. Finally Whitehead defines a plane in the timeless space of a time-system "a" as the locus of all those points of the space which intersect any moment in event-particles lying on a single level with the moment.

In summary:

Type of Space	Instantaneous space	Space time	Timeless space
Physical Status	Ideal limits of perceptual spaces as time is decreased	4-dimensional space-time of Minkowski	Space of physics
Points	Puncts	event-particles	point (point-tracks of a parallel family)
Lines	Rects	point-tracks null-tracks sets of co-rect event-particles	straight lines (comatricial sets of parallel point-tracks)
Planes	Levels	Matrices (sets of co-level event-particles)	plane

158

After defining congruence, Whitehead derives
the transformation equations of the special theory of
relativity and develops a law of gravitation. In his
derivation of the Lorentz-Einstein formulae, Whitehead
never makes use of the velocity of light. He has
simply used considerations about events, (their overlapping, their cogredience with durations); the
definitions of congruence and normality; and the
assumption about the velocity of one system in the
space of another. It is only in this last stage that
we ask what particular value to give the constant "k"
which will give us a system of kinematics that fits
the facts. If we assign the value of the velocity of
light to "k" we achieve the desired system.

Resolution of the Debates

The Method as a Mathematical Model

This study has been an attempt to establish
that the method of extensive abstraction is, according
to the contemporary norms of model theory, an algebraic
mathematical model. The essential characteristic of
such a model is that it possesses the property of similarity of structure with the theory which it models.
This similarity of structure is referred to technically
as the property of isomorphism. A model is isomorphic
with the theory it models when there exists a mapping
function which sets up a correspondence between each
element of one set with one and only one member
(called the image) of the other set. Not only must
a correspondence between entities be accomplished, but
there must also be a correspondence between the relations
existing between the entities of each set. For example,
if the members of the first set stand in the relation R to
each other, then the images of these members must stand
in the relation S which is the image of the R relation.
If such conditions are fulfilled the model is the
classical or general isomorphic form. Because some
scientific and mathematical models fall short of the
stated norms, but do, nevertheless, fulfill one or
several functions of scientific models such as quanti-
fication, simplifaction, or globalisation, attempts have
recently been made to formalize a theory of approximative algebraic isomorphisms which would include all
these models which fall short of meeting the strict

requirements of classical isomorphism.

In Chapter IV of this paper, we have drawn two
conclusions concerning the status of extensive abstraction as a mathematical model. If we think of the method
as an isomorphism between <u>perceived</u> natural entities
and mathematical entities such as points, instants,
lines, etc., the method comes off as a classical algebraic
model. This is so only because we have previously established that the process of perception endows natural
entities with definiteness and exactness by means of the
cogitative element present in the perceptual process. If,
however, we insist that the method is a correspondence
between natural entities as they exist in nature and the
mathematical elements, then the method falls short of the
strict requirements of a classical isomorphism. Although
Whitehead believed in the uniformity of nature, this
assertion is a far cry from establishing that this means
that he held that the relations of nature are exact and
necessary. A more probable interpretation is that Whitehead believed nature to be <u>potentially</u> exact and definite
(capable of supporting a deduced superstructure which is
logical and mathematical in character) but is <u>actually</u>
inexact and indefinite. Only through the processes of
perception and extensive abstraction are natural entities
rendered fit for scientific use. Therefore, as a
correspondence between mathematical entities and natural
entities as they are in nature, the method of extensive
abstraction is an <u>approximative</u> algebraic isomorphic
model.

We will now recall the main charges of V. F.
Lenzen, A. Grunbaum, and E. Nagel against the success
and validity of the method, in the hopes that by applying
the conclusions flowing from the status of the method as
a mathematical model, we can support Whitehead's utilization of the method as a means of avoiding the bifurcation
of nature which he so often and so rightly criticized.

V. F. Lenzen

In "Scientific Ideas and Experience" Lenzen
made several major charges against Whitehead's method.
First he believed that Whitehead was inconsistent in his
use of the term "ultimate fact." It sometimes meant a
fundamental <u>concept</u>, and at other times it meant fundamental <u>data</u>. However, this shows a misunderstanding of

160

Whitehead's theory of perception. Perception does involve an intellectual element which endows sense data with exactness. Perceptual judgments occur instinctively. This is, most likely, what Whitehead intended when he used the term "fundamental concept." It must be admitted, however, that though Whitehead was leaning towards naive realism during his philosophy of nature period, strains of sensationalist perception theory remain throughout his phenomenalistic expositions.

Secondly, Lenzen objects to Whitehead's use of durations of unlimited temporal extent in the derivation of a moment.(1) Durations and especially abstractive classes of durations made up of members below the threshold of thought are not apprehended in sense-awareness but are constructs of thought. Lenzen fails to realize that Whitehead was well aware that abstractive classes were not given in sense-awareness. His method of extensive abstraction was a mathematical construction which was to mathematize and simplify, by means of iso-morphic correspondences between mathematical entities and natural entities, a theory of space-time. Abstractive classes are exact mathematical entities corresponding to the experienced and perceived natural entities. Since the method has been judged to be a valid mathematical model, the use of abstractive classes with no smallest minimal member is permissible. The same reasoning can be applied to Lenzen's objections against Whitehead's use of an infinite set of elements and elements having a temporal thickness less than the threshold value of human perception. As for the criticism that elements with definiteness are not given in sense-awareness, we answer by again pointing out that if we interpret "sense-awareness" to include the complete process of perception (as Whitehead many times did so use the phrase), then this is not a true reading of Whitehead's theory of perception. Perception endowed elements with definiteness. Yet, taking "sense-awareness" to mean only sense-presentation of the very first crude reception of sense data prior to the instinctive perceptual judgment, then we must grant Lenzen his point.

Adolf Grünbaum

Grünbaum poses three major objections to the method of extensive abstraction. He asserts that, in

order for intervals to be considered as aggregates of
unextended points and instants, a super-denumerable
infinity of perceivables must be possible. But,
obviously, this is beyond the limitations of human
perceptual powers. Secondly, Grunbaum states that the
method obliterates precision of meaning since it is
grounded on sense perception which provides no means
for distinguishing the abstractive classes required
to confer a separate identity upon points very close to
each other such as the points $x = 0$ and $x = 10^{-1000}$.
Thirdly, since abstractive classes contain an infinite
number of regions, they, too, are beyond the domain of
sense-awareness. All of Grunbaum's criticisms can be
reduced to this--that the mathematical entities and
techniques used in the method are not given in sense
perception. And, Grunbaum assumes, this is what Whitehead
had claimed was the case. But, with Wolfe Mays, we
respond by saying that this is a misinterpretation of
Whitehead who, unfortunately, did not always make it
sufficiently clear that his method was to be taken as a
mathematical construction and not as an exact description of some actual process of convergence. From the
conclusion reached in this study, we can justify Whitehead's use of mathematical processes involving infinity,
convergence, etc. Therefore, we concur with Mays in
asserting that the general position held by Whitehead is
that he was not trying to construct a geometry from sense
experience, but using a mathematical model to clarify
certain relations appearing in perception.

Ernest Nagel

The issues raised by Nagel in objection to Whitehead's method of extensive abstraction are similar to
Grunbaum's. First, no empirically given subject matter
involves infinite sets of volumes. Secondly, no experimenter could ever test to see if a point is a point since
to do this he would be required to understand relations
between an infinite set of objects. Thirdly, the method
fails to explain how any of the scientific concepts
defined by infinite series or limiting processes are
connected to or applied to subject matter.

The first objection has already been answered
by our response to Grunbaum. Victor Lowe has satisfactorily responded to the second objection by asking

what kind of something could ever be subjected to such a
test. A true point can never be observed ! To claim that
Whitehead would think that they ever could be would be
absurd. Nagel's third objection is a bit more difficult,
but it, too, can be met by an appeal to the status of
the method as a mathematical model. The method does not
fully explain how scientific concepts defined by infinite
series or limiting processes are connected to subject
matter, but these are mathematical techniques which "guide
thought." We begin with events in nature and by means of
abstraction, seek some way to define an event without any
extension. As an "intermediary model" between the abstract
world of science and the concrete world, the method does
have real value.

Robert Palter

As the recognized authority on the technical
aspects of Whitehead's philosophy of science, Robert
Palter's reflections on the philosophical import of the
method of extensive abstraction cannot be overlooked.
I shall attempt to summarize his position briefly but
adequately.(2)

Palter admits that the criticism that the method
presupposes as ultimate entities sharply bounded events
which are not in fact available to sense perception, has
a certain force. But, he adds, this in no way diminishes
the value of what Whitehead has accomplished in his attempt
to develop geometry and kinematics on a more concrete
basis. It does suggest a possible direction for further
technical innovations, namely, the introduction of ultimate
entities which are not assumed to possess sharply defined
boundaries. However, if we grant that perception does
endow events with sharp boundaries, we diminish the force
of the unfavorable criticism.

Palter also states that the axioms of the method
should be confirmable by direct perception. They cannot
be directly confirmed by physical measurement since the
axioms are in all respects prior to actual measuring procedures. The proper interpretation of Whitehead's
assertion that axioms are laws of nature depending on
empirical verification is that there are certain elements
together with their interrelations given in perception of
which these axioms are the idealized and generalized
counterparts. This reflection by Palter fits in perfectly

163

with our proposal that the method is an isomorphism
setting up the correspondence between the natural elements
and their idealized mathematical counterparts.

Since some of the events in an abstractive class
are perceived through the senses as extending over one
another, says Palter, the general concepts of events and
of extension between events are clear enough to make the
search for convergence to simplicity an "instinctive
procedure of habitual experience." This instinctive
procedure is lifted to the level of reflective awareness
by the method of extensive abstraction without any serious
loss of contact with immediate sense experience. Abstractive classes "guide thought" in directions determined by
sense-perception but to destinations beyond all possibility
of detection by sense perception. These destinations are
the abstractions of science, entities which are truly in
nature, though they have no meaning in isolation from
nature. Again, the conclusions of this study reinforce
Palter's opinions.

Palter does see difficulty in reconciling
Whitehead's insistence on direct perception as the source
of scientific concepts with his complex logical and
mathematical devices for constructing and elaborating
these concepts. Yet, the difficulty is lessened somewhat
if we think of the method with all its logical and mathematical devices as a model of the relationships apparent
among natural entities.

Palter points out one serious dilemma concerning Whitehead's assumption of the existence of alternative
time-systems in nature (in which case Whitehead should
show how direct sense perception furnishes evidence for
this assumption). If this can't be done then Whitehead's
procedure depends only on the assumption of the mere
abstract possibility of alternative time-systems in nature.
But Whitehead admits that direct sense perception furnishes
no evidence for the actual existence of different time-
systems, and yet he wishes to account for the actual
concepts of space, time, and motion, and some of the
actual experimental results of contemporary physics which
depend on a variety of time-systems.

Palter gives two possible (but not equally
forceful) ways of resolving the dilemma. He admits that
both are unsatisfactory from the point of view of

164

of Whitehead's natural philosophy. On the one hand, we might accept the multiplicity of time-systems as a mere possibility; but then Whitehead's entire procedure seems to become little else than a more or less impressive logico-mathematical technique without any clear-cut relevance to the concepts and theories of contemporary physics. Or we may take the existence of multiple time-systems in nature as a fundamental principle of natural philosophy (whether warranted by direct sense-perception or not). This latter alternative, says Palter, is clearly incompatible with some of Whitehead's remarks. Whitehead himself says that the metaphysical hypothesis of multiple time-systems is introduced in order "to satisfy the present demands of scientific hypothesis."(3) This means that Whitehead did not mean the hypothesis to be a fundamental datum of sense perception. This leaves us with the first alternative. Palter does not want to admit this as being the status of the method and therefore says the dilemma is unresolved. However, we believe that the method as a model is an impressive logico-mathematical technique which does have correspondence (and therefore relevance) to the concepts of physics. Since we can validly employ mathematical hypotheses in this model, why cannot we also employ the hypothesis of hyperbolic kinematics (alternative time-systems)?

Palter concludes that no matter what our thinking may be as to the value of Whitehead's method it is clear that we are dealing with a critical issue in Western philosophy, namely, the question of the kind and degree of influence which science should exert on philosophy. Palter believes that Whitehead's philosophy of science attempts to transcend the particularities of current science and somehow to illuminate or make intelligible these very particularities.

Concluding remark

It is apparent to any serious student of Whitehead's philosophy of science that his method of extensive abstraction has several flaws. The greatest difficulty is the assumption of alternative time-systems in nature. Yet, the method is Whitehead's greatest contribution to philosophy of science, a contribution which has been discussed and criticized by many scholars. Many of the

165

charges and objections made by Whitehead's critics,
however, can be satisfactorily refuted by the acceptance
of the method as a mathematical model--a modern replacement of the static Newtonian world concept by a
multi-relationed mathematical concept of a world in
process.

NOTES

1. As was pointed out in Chapter I of this paper,
this is a misinterpretation on Lenzen's part.
Cf. p. 21.

2. Palter, pp. 99-105

APPENDIX

"THE RELATIONAL THEORY OF SPACE"
Alfred North Whitehead
(Translated by Janet Fitzgerald)

I.   The Different Meanings of the Word "Space"

It is important to distinguish four different
meanings which are included in the use of the word "space."
These distinctions of meaning extend to the word geometry
in the measure in which the latter is defined as the
science of the properties of space.

To begin it is necessary to make a primary
distinction between "apparent space" and "physical space."
Apparent space is the place of objects insofar as they
appear to us. It is the space in which green trees,
sounds, odors are perceived. If we accept the idea that
space is nothing else but a complex of certain relations
among objects, then apparent space is a complex of
certain relations among perceived objects.

We shall call these perceived objects apparent
objects. Apparent space is then the space of apparent
objects. An apparent object is necessarily a function of
a perceiver. The apparent space of A is, naturally,
different from the apparent space of B. In fact, the
apparent space of A consists only of certain relations
among the things which appear to A; the apparent space
of B consists only of certain relations among the things
which appear to B.

Two meanings must be distinguished in the words
"apparent space." "Immediate apparent space" is that
which appears immediately to the perceiver; it is exactly
that which appears as directly perceived. This may be
from a part of a room to a slope of a mountain with some
objects in between [the perceiver and the mountain] .
It is the immediate and fragmentary appearance of the
world to a perceiver.

"Complete apparent space" is the idea of the total space of a world complete with apparent objects in which one no longer refers exclusively to a perceiving subject. This manner of "completing" presents a double character. In the first place, the immediate apparent spaces of different individuals are adjusted one to the other, the golden side and the silver side of a buckle are combined into a unique object. In the second place, one forms, however grossly, an idea of a physical world, and the apparent world is then completed by the adjunction of the idea of all the perceptions which could be apparent to some hypothetical subjects in accordance with the laws and the state of the physical world. This conception [of a complete apparent world] , thus completed in a double sense, includes the world of apparent objects in an apparent limitless space. Complete apparent space is the space of the perceived world to which men commonly refer in conversation. It is ordinarily conceived as unique. For example, in a court of law testimony concerning the presence of a red rug in an empty room would never be rejected as being without interest under the pretext that it would be equally possible to "complete" the universe with or without the rug. Complete apparent space assumes the conception of a "physical world" which we must now examine.

Physical space is the space of a hypothetical world, the same for all, of objects whose relations would correspond exactly to our sensations. That which appears immediately to a subject is, in this case, related to a complex of relations among physical objects. For example, a visual sensation is related to an excitation of the brain, which comes from an excitation of the nerves of the retina of the eye, which itself comes from an impact of light rays, etc.

The exact analysis of the essential logical process which is involved in this parallelism and of the fundamental ideas which have led the human race to it cannot enter within the domain of this treatise. We mention it as a fundamental scientific problem which we here lay aside.

This parallelism is habitually presented as a "causation" of sensations by the states of the physical

168

world. But the only essential characteristic of this
physical world is the parallelism of its events with the
perceptions of all known subjects. It is evident that
such a world is a hypothetical logical construction.

The objects of this physical world will be
called "physical objects." According to common physics,
perceptions result from the changing relations among
physical objects occurring in a given lapse of time.
For example, visual sensation results from an impact of
a number of ether waves upon the eye, sound comes from
the impact of a number of air waves on the tympanum and
it is the same with other sensations. Therefore,
apparent objects of an apparent world are in direct
correlation with the <u>events</u> of the physical world and
not with the objects of the physical world. The conse-
quence of this is that, by thought, the apparent fluid
objects are replaced and are broken up into more permanent
physical objects; all progress in the analysis of the
physical world consists in replacing unstable objects by
permanent objects. For example, apparent bodies are
replaced by physical molecules, molecules by atoms, atoms
by electrons. And each time that such a replacement takes
place, the properties of relatively complex bodies are
conceived as the properties of <u>events</u>, occurring in an
ensemble of more simple component parts in interaction.

The fourth use of the word "space" is that of
"abstract space," and the science that corresponds to it
is abstract geometry.

Geometry, as a mathematical science, is
necessarily abstract geometry. Indeed, in all mathematical
research, the research is essentially general although a
particular application may be the sole end by reason of
its importance. The conclusions of propositions are true
for any group of entities whatever for which the hypotheses
are true. Applied geometry, like all applied mathematics,
is simply pure geometry, the predominant application of
which preoccupies us.

Thus the four meanings of the word "space" are
distinguished by the terms "immediate apparent space,"
"complete apparent space," "physical space," and "abstract
space."

There are numerous immediate apparent spaces
and numerous abstract spaces. It is customary to
suppose that there is only one complete apparent space
and one physical space.

The belief in the unity of complete apparent
space seems justifiable. But the belief in the unity
of physical space calls for reservations in the measure
in which space is considered as consisting simply of
certain properties of a complex of relations among
physical objects it will certainly be possible to
construct different complexes of relations which will
give place to different definitions of points, lines,
planes, etc., with the logical type of properties which
are defined as spatial.

But in physics there is surely a dominant
interest in a certain complex of relations which will
then form physical space as a function of which all
physical action is expressed. Thus in a practical
sense there is only one physical space; in a theoretical
sense, there is an infinite number of them.

II. Physical Objects and Physical Space

Physical space is the space of physical science,
the space in which electrons and molecules move and act
one on the other or by the medium of the ether.

The physical world exists in time and the time
of the physical world is identical with the time of the
complete apparent world and [with the time of] the various
immediate apparent worlds of different perceiving subjects. Common time is the place in which the parallelism
of the different worlds is safeguarded and made possible.
It is evident that, on this point, the real problem of
time is the formation of a common time for the complete
apparent world, outside [that of] the different times of
the immediate apparent worlds of various perceiving
subjects.

Relations among physical objects can be divided
into two classes: direct relations and indirect relations.
If A is related to B and B to C, then the very fact of

these two relations constitutes an indirect relation of A to C. But the indirect relations suppose direct relations, which themselves are no longer decomposable. The first problem of the determination of the physical world is to determine certain general characteristics of these direct relations and of the related objects.

Direct relations between physical objects are, by hypothesis, determined by their relations with some antecedent part of time. Therefore, considering dynamically in connection with subsequent time, they [direct relations] are the causes of future events. From this last point of view they are conceived as the actions of objects one upon the other causing the direct relations of subsequent moments. But the actions among physical objects are not different relations from caused relations. There is only one type of fact to be considered, namely that the state of the physical universe across a certain lapse of time determines subsequent states. Consequently, the direct relations of physical objects during a certain lapse of time are conceived as the active agents in the appearance of subsequent states, and thus conceived are called "actions of objects one upon the other."

In order to show the necessity of a minute analysis of our ideas on spatial relations, let us consider the three primary axioms which often, implicity or explicity, govern thought on this subject. These three axioms are:

1) An object cannot be entirely in two places at the same time in such a manner as to be entirely in each of these two places.

(2) Two objects cannot be in the same place at the same time.

(3) Two objects at a distance cannot act one upon the other.

If we maintain the last two axioms, it follows that no action is possible between two different objects. For it they are at the same point, they are the same object; and if they are at different points, they are at

171

a distance and cannot therefore act one upon the other.

Moreover, if the first and the third axioms are maintained and the second discarded, then action between distinct objects is possible, namely between the objects which are all at the same point. But in virtue of the preceding argument, no action is possible between objects at different points. Thus each point would contain a completely independent world from the world of other points.

The preceiding reasoning is not generally admitted. One faces the question whether the hypothesis of continuity of matter through space permits action to be transmitted without denying action at a distance. In this alternative the action is transmitted by the contiguous particles in a continuous medium. Any two points are separated by a distance and consequently, according to the third axiom, the parts of the medium cannot act upon each other in any couple of points.

One can further say that action begins at the limit as the distance between two points becomes infinitely small. But this rests on an erroneous conception of the theory of limits condemned by Weierstrass. There are no infinitely small distances. All distance is finite and if the matter of two separated points act one upon the other they act across a finite distance.

One can further claim that action is not between matter reduced to points, but between matter occupying volumes, and that there are contiguous volumes.

However, let us consider the common limit of two contiguous volumes. Action is produced only across this limit. But there are no infinitely small volumes. We have then two finite volumes acting on each other across their common limit. Now two finite volumes can be divided into two parts. Any position of one or the other volume which can be included in a non-contiguous position to the limit does not contribute to the action; for it is at a distance from the limit. But then all the matter surrounding any point which is not on the limit does not contribute to the action. Then there is no matter occupying a volume which contributes in any fashion to the action. The action is then due to the matter of the

172

point situated on the limit.   But this action has been
shown impossible.

The objection can be avoided by affirming
that when the volumes are reduced to a certain degree,
the action between contiguous volumes must be related
to each volume taken as a whole and cannot be calculated
as the sum of the separate actions of the parts of the
volume.   If one holds to this position one must face
two sorts of considerations.

(a)   Since there are no infinitely small volumes, the
limit of extent must be finite.   Then one must admit
an atomic structure of the continuous medium, in such a
way that the medium is composed of ultimate finite
elements which act as wholes on contiguous elements.
Thus, the elements although they are ideally geometri-
cally divisible, are as far as the question of physical
action is concerned, indivisible.

(b)   This atomic structure of the medium having been
admitted, two atomic volumes cannot be contiguous
unless one of the two is without surface.   For there are
no contiguous points, and consequently, there are no
contiguous points on two distinct limits.

Then, according to (a) and (b), the only
continuous medium which can transmit action according
to the three previously cited axioms is the medium composed of atomic finite elements in such a way that all
the atomic elements with surfaces are mixed with atomic
elements without surfaces.

This conception is logically possible, it is
very improbable and has never, as a matter of fact, been
adopted.

The real objection, however, is not the im-
probability of the conception to which the three axioms
lead, but rather the non-analyzed and non-critical conceptions of space and of objects from which it proceeds.

To deny action at a distance is indeed to deny
the direct relations between physical objects not
occupying the same points; but that implies the negation

173

of the theory of space-relation. For it is difficult to
see how space can be constituted by relations between
objects which are not related. To deny action at a
distance can only suit the relational theory on the
condition that the relations between physical objects
from which proceed spatial relations are not part of
those relations which are the antecedents of changes of
spatial relations in subsequent times. This perhaps is
true, but it is rash to erect this principle as an
"a priori" axiom of science.

III. The Relational Theory of Space

Geometry as a mathematical theory has usually
taken as a point of departure all or part of the fundamental spatial entities, points, curved or straight
lines, surfaces, and volumes. It takes them as simple
primitive ideas, i.e. in abstract language as "variables"
which are not logical functions of more simple variables.
But if the relational theory of space is adopted either
for the apparent world or for the physical world, this
cannot be the first stage of geometric research. For
the relative theory of space, it is essential that points,
for example, be complex entities, logical functions of
those relations between objects constituting space. For,
if a point is a simple thing, incapable of being logically defined by means of relations among objects, then
the points are indeed absolute positions. Then the
relation of "being at a point" must be a primitive relation incapable of definition, and thus, one must take as
the only ultimate fact of geometry the primitive relations
of objects to their absolute positions. But this is
nothing else than the absolute theory of space which,
nominally at least, has almost universally been abandoned.
Then, the first occupation of geometricians searching for
the foundations of their science is to define points as
functions of relations between objects.

The fundamental order of ideas is first a
world of things in relation, then space whose fundamental
entities are defined by means of these relations, and
whose properties are deduced from the nature of these
relations. The ultimate elements of the world thus put
in relation do not necessarily have to "occupy" a position

174

in space in order to have <u>unique</u> positions in space.
At least this hypothesis is not at all necessary in
the relational theory. It is necessary up to a certain
point for apparent space, since some of these "things"
are apparent objects and must, by the same token, be
perceived in apparent space. But the perceiving
subjects are not already bound to any assignable
position. As for physical space, it is possible that
molecules, electrons, the ether of physics are very
well conceived as derived complex objects, while the
fundamental physical objects, i.e. the terms fixed by
the simplest relations can have no connection with
definite positions in space. Whatever be the physical
theory finally adopted by science, physical objects
"in space' simple or derived must be admitted by it.
In the relational theory of space, we do not have to
consider these physical bodies as first existing in space
and then acting one upon the other directly or indirectly.
They are in space because they act one upon the other,
and space is nothing else than the expression of certain
properties of their interaction. A geometry book, insofar
as it treats geometry as a science applicable to physical
space, is nothing else but the first part of a treatise
of physics. Its subject is not "the introduction to
Physics," but it is Physics.

        The fundamental idea from which springs the
relative theory in its construction of a concept of a
world existing in space is that of a class of relations
(s).(1) Starting with any class (s) of relations, let
us find those possible definitions of some fundamental
spatial concepts and what properties which (s) must have
in order that the usual propositions can be true of the
concepts thus defined. A world, thus founded on a (s)
class will be called an "s-world."

. . . .

        In apparent space a point is, practically
speaking, an area or a volume sufficiently small so that
the subject is incapable of introducing into it an exact
division into parts. From such "minima sensibilia"
neither surface nor volume are wanting but the stability
necessary for division. The same in physical space; a
point is, practically speaking, an area or a volume

175

sufficiently small such that a division is useless in
the actual state of science.

But those are approximative usages of the
concept of "point." Exact deductive science has progressed by substituting exact concepts for approximative
ones. For example, geometry has inaugurated its
brilliant progress by employing in the true sense the
idea of a point; that which has essentially and exactly
neither parts nor extension. . . .

The simplicity of exact reasoning does not
depend on the logical simplicity of the concepts which
it employs. It depends on the fact that the laws which
govern the logical combinations and its concepts are
simple and in particular they are perfectly general.
. . . Thus, in a deductive science, one does not look
for logical simplicity in the concept of the entities
which form the field of thought, but the simplicity
and generality in the relations by which these entities
are brought together. Better still, in order that an
exact science thus obtained be really important in the
sphere of thought from which it is derived, it is necessary that an approximative interpretation of its exact
theorems be possible in the primitive domain of concepts.

By applying these remarks to geometry we see
that we have no need for a simple logical definition of
points, lines, and surfaces, but the definitions which
keep the general and simple properties which are
attributed to them in geometry and which permit us at
the same time to substitute for them approximative concepts of points (for example) in the approximative
propositions of simpler domains of thought where the
fundamental concepts appear.

IV. The Relations of Whole-to-Part and s-Inclusion

. . . .

(5) Every spatial object has spatial parts
other than itself. This property of spatial "whole and
part" is the hypothesis of infinite divisibility; it is
the foundation of the continuity of space. The truth of

176

the proposition is not evident. In apparent space the
existence of minima visibilia seems to contradict it.
In the physical world, the hypothesis of continuity makes
mathematical deductions possible in the present state of
mathematical knowledge, but there is no well defined
reason to adopt it [the hypothesis] except for its
convenience.

. . . .

V. The Relational Definition of Spatial Concepts

. . . .

        The general conception which now has to be
stated precisely is that of an object progressively cut
into smaller and smaller parts until its dimensions have
disappeared and there remains only one point. According
to this conception, a point is sometimes called a
"conceptual limit" obtained by the preceding procedure.
It is easy to establish the general nature of this concept
of a point by means of s-objects and the relation E_s.
[s-inclusion]

        Let us consider a series x_1, x_2, x_3 . . . of
an infinite number of s-objects such that $x_1 E_s x_2$,
$x_2 E_s x_3$ . . . and finally x_1, x_2, x_3 . . . converge
towards a conceptual limit which does not have parts.
It is evident that the two critical words on which the
meaning of the process here described depends still have
no determined meaning. The meaning of "convergence" of
an infinite series of numbers is precise and definite.
But s-objects are not numbers and the mathematical meaning
of "convergence" does not simply apply.

        Moreover, what is the meaning here of a limit?
The "limit" of a function in Analysis has an exact meaning which does not apply here. There is another, more
general meaning of the word "limit," namely the sense in
which G. Cantor employed the term of "point-limits" of a
series (Cf. Princ. mat., *207). But this conception is
not useful for us here.

. . . .

177

VI. Geometric T-Serial and T-Equal Classes

. . . .

Apparent objects are perceived as <u>areas</u>, not
necessarily as planes. The interior of these objects is
conceived, but the immediate apprehension is always the
perception of a surface object. In the measure in which
the points are directly perceived, it must be by the
perception of an indivisible point area. Then, if the
relations of two surface objects are <u>perceived</u> as exactly
defined by a geometric point, then an indivisible point
area is perceived as the point which defines this relation.

. . . .

The foundation of this reasoning is that geometric points
or lines are not given in perception but are the result
of a <u>concept</u> of a geometric series. The areas, containing
one another, are not exactly defined in perception by the
homogeneous parts of surfaces; they exist only as <u>possi-
bilities</u> of sub-division. There are or (there can be
according to the logical theory here developed) exceptional
points and lines which are objects of perception. From
this comes the possibility of defined common limits for all
the areas of a series. But when the law of convergence
requires in its definition a definite point or a definite
line, this point or this line must be a perceived point
or a perceived line; consequently, the perceived point
must be an indivisible, perceived point area. Outside of
these exceptional cases which our reasoning includes, the
convergence is essentially made towards a <u>determined</u>
point or a <u>determined</u> line in the interior of each member
of the series. . . . The general result of the theory
is that, although a point be (in exceptional cases)
directly perceived, it is in general simply the concept of
the possibility of a series of subdivisions. It is the
same for a line or a line segment. . . . .

. . . .

NOTES

1. The Roman letter "s" is used instead of the Greek
"sigma" for typographical purposes.

178

BIBLIOGRAPHY

Primary Sources

Books

Whitehead, Alfred North. Adventures of Ideas.
New York: The Macmillan Company, 1933

_____. The Aims of Education, and Other Essays.
New York: The Free Press, 1967.

_____. Alfred North Whitehead: An Anthology.
Edited by F. S. C. Northrop and Mason W. Gross.
New York: The Macmillan Company, 1953.

_____. The Concept of Nature. Cambridge: At the
University Press, 1955.

_____. An Enquiry Concerning the Principles of
Natural Knowledge. Cambridge: At the
University Press, 1955.

_____. Essays in Science and Philosophy. New York;
Philosophical Library, 1948.

_____. The Function of Reason. Boston: Beacon
Press, 1967.

_____. An Interpretation of Science: Selected
Essays. Edited by A. H. Johnson. ("Liberal
Arts Press Book.") Indianapolis: The Bobbs-
Merrill Company, Inc., 1961.

_____. An Introduction to Mathematics. New York:
Oxford University Press, 1958.

_____. _Modes of Thought_. New York: The Free
Press, 1968.

_____. _The Organisation of Thought, Educational and
Scientific_. London: Williams & Norgate, Ltd.,
1917.

_____. _Principia Mathematica_. With Bertrand Russell,
F. R. S. Vol. I. 2nd ed. to *56. Cambridge:
At the University Press, 1967.

_____. The _Principle of Relativity_. Cambridge:
Cambridge University Press, 1922.

_____. _Process and Reality: An Essay in Cosmology_.
New York: Harper & Brothers, 1960.

_____. _Science and the Modern World_. New York:
Macmillan Company, 1925.

_____. _Symbolism, Its Meaning and Effect_. New York:
Capricorn Books, 1959.

_____. _A Treatise on Universal Algebra_. New York:
Hafner Publishing Company, 1960.

Essays

_____. "The Anatomy of Some Scientific Ideas,"
in _The Aims of Education_, Chap. IX.

_____. "Autobiographical Notes," in _The Philosophy
of Alfred North Whitehead_ (edited by Paul
Arthur Schilpp), pp. 3-14.

_____. "The Axioms of Descriptive Geometry,"
_Cambridge Tracts in Mathematics and Mathematical
Physics_, No. 5. New York: Hafner Publishing
Company, 1907.

_____. "The Idealistic Interpretation of Einstein's
Theory," in _The Interpretation of Science:
Selected Essays_ (edited by A. H. Johnson),
pp. 145-48.

_____ . "On Mathematical Concepts of the Material World," in Alfred North Whitehead: An Anthology (edited by F. S. C. Northrop and Mason W. Gross), pp. 7-82.

_____ . "The Organisation of Thought," in The Aims of Education, Chap. VIII.

_____ . "The Philosophical Aspects of the Principle of Relativity," in The Interpretation of Science: Selected Essays (edited by A. H. Johnson), pp. 136-44.

_____ . "The Problem of Simultaneity," in The Interpretation of Science: Selected Essays (edited by A. H. Johnson), pp. 149-56.

_____ . "Remarks," Philosophical Review XLVI (1937), pp. 178-86.

_____ . "Space, Time, and Relativity," in The Interpretation of Science: Selected Essays (edited by A. H. Johnson), pp. 90-107.

_____ . "La Théorie Relationniste de l'Espace," Revue de Metaphysique et de Morale, XXIII (May, 1916), pp. 423-54.

_____ . "Time," in The Interpretation of Science: Selected Essays (edited by A. H. Johnson), pp. 240-47.

_____ . "Time, Space, and Material: Are They, and If So in What Sense, the Ultimate Data of Science?" in The Interpretation of Science: Selected Essays (edited by A. H. Johnson), pp. 56-68.

_____ . "Uniformity and Contingency," in The Interpretation of Science: Selected Essays (edited by A. H. Johnson), pp. 108-24.

Secondary Sources

Books

Abian, Alexander. The Theory of Sets and Transfinite Arithmetic. Philadelphia and London: W. B. Saunders Company, 1965.

Alexander, S. Space, Time, and Deity. 2 vols. London: Macmillan and Company, Ltd., 1920.

Black, Max. Models and Metaphors. Ithaca, New York: Cornell University Press, 1962.

_____. The Nature of Mathematics. Patterson: Littlefield, Adams & Co., 1959.

Bright, Lawrence, O. P. Whitehead's Philosophy of Physics. London: Sheed and Ward, 1958.

Broad, C. D. Perception, Physics, and Reality. Cambridge: At the University Press, 1914.

_____. Scientific Thought. London: Routledge & Kegan Paul, Ltd., 1923.

Christian, William A. An Interpretation of Whitehead's Metaphysics. New Haven: Yale University Press, 1959.

Grünbaum, Adolf. Philosophical Problems of Space and Time. New York: Alfred A. Knopf, 1963.

Hammerschmidt, W. W. Whitehead's Philosophy of Time. New York: King's Crown Press, 1947.

Hesse, Mary B. Models and Analogues in Science. Notre Dame: University of Notre Dame Press, 1966.

International Union of History and Philosophy of Science. The Concept and the Role of the Model in Mathematics and Natural and Social Sciences. Proceedings of the Colloquium sponsored by the Division of Philosophy of Sciences. New York: Gordon and Breach Science Publishers, 1961.

Johnson, A. H. Whitehead's Theory of Reality. New
    York: Dover Publications, Inc., 1962.

Kline, George L. (ed.). Alfred North Whitehead:
    Essays on His Philosophy. Englewood Cliffs,
    N. J.: Prentice-Hall, Inc., 1963.

Körner, S. The Philosophy of Mathematics. New York:
    Harper & Brothers, 1960.

Lawrence, Nathaniel. Whitehead's Philosophical Develop-
    ment. Berkeley: University of California Press
    Press, 1956.

Leclerc, Ivor (ed.). The Relevance of Whitehead:
    Philosophical Essays in Commemoration of the
    Centenary of the Birth of Alfred North Whitehead.
    London: George Allen & Unwin, Ltd., 1961.

_____. Whitehead's Metaphysics: An Introductory
    Exposition. London: George Allen and Unwin,
    Ltd., 1958.

Lowe, Victor. Understanding Whitehead. Baltimore:
    The Johns Hopkins Press, 1962.

_____. Harthshorne, Charles, and Johnson, A. H.
    Whitehead and the Modern World. Boston: The
    Beacon Press, 1950.

Mays, Wolfe. The Philosophy of Whitehead. London:
    George Allen & Unwin, Ltd., 1959.

Nagel, Ernest. Sovereign Reason. Glencoe, Illinois:
    Free Press, 1954.

_____. The Structure of Science: Problems in the
    Logic of Scientific Explanation. New York:
    Harcourt, Brace & World, Inc., 1961.

Nicod, Jean. Foundations of Geometry and Induction.
    Translated by P. P. Wiener. London: Routledge
    & Kegan Paul, Ltd., 1930.

Palter, Robert M. Whitehead's Philosophy of Science.
    Chicago: The University of Chicago Press, 1960.

Poincaré, Henri. Science and Hypothesis. New York: Dover Publications, 1952.

Price, Lucien. Dialogues of Alfred North Whitehead, As Recorded by Lucien Price. New York: Mentor Books by arrangement with Little, Brown, and Company, 1954.

Reese, William and Freeman (editors). Process and Divinity, The Hartshorne Fetschrift. LaSalle, Illinois: Open Court Publishing Company, 1964.

Russell, Bertrand. Our Knowledge of the External World. New York: Mentor Books by arrangement with George Allen & Unwin, Ltd., 1960.

_____. Portraits from Memory, and Other Essays. New York: Simon and Schuster, 1956.

_____. The Principles of Mathematics. London: George Allen & Unwin Ltd., 1903.

Schilpp, Paul Arthur (ed.). Albert Einstein: Philosopher-Scientist. "The Library of Living Philosophers, Vol. VII." Evanston and Chicago: Northwestern University Press, 1949.

_____. The Philosophy of Alfred North Whitehead. "The Library of Living Philosophers, Vol. III." Evanston and Chicago: Northwestern University Press, 1941.

Schmidt, Paul. Perception and Cosmology in Whitehead's Philosophy. New Brunswick, N. J.: Rutgers University Press, 1967.

Wells, Harry Kohlsaat. Process and Unreality: A Criticism of Method in Whitehead's Philosophy. New York: King's Crown Press, 1950.

Articles

Alston, William. "Whitehead's Denial of Simple Location," Journal of Philosophy, XLVIII (1951), 713-21.

Apostel, Leo. "Toward the Formal Study of Models in the
    Non-Formal Sciences," in The Concept and the Role
    of the Model in Mathematics and Natural and
    Social Sciences, pp. 1-37.

Ballard, Edward G. "Kant and Whitehead, and the Philoso-
    phy of Mathematics," Tulane Studies in Philosophy,
    Vol. X, 2-29.

Broad, C. D. "Critical Notices: The Principles of
    Natural Knowledge by A. N. Whitehead," Mind,
    XXIX (1920), 216-31.

_____. "Critical Notices: The Principle of Relativity
    by A. N. Whitehead," Mind, XXXII (1923),
    211-19.

Chiaraviglio, Lucio. "Extension and Abstraction," in
    Process and Divinity (edited by Reese and
    Freeman), pp. 205-16.

Grünbaum, Adolf. "Whitehead's Method of Extensive Ab-
    straction," British Journal for the Philosophy of
    Science, IV (1953-54), 215-26.

Harrah, David. "The Influence of Logic and Mathematics on
    Whitehead," Journal of the History of Ideas,
    XX (1959), 420-30.

Hartshorne, Charles. "Whitehead and Contemporary Philoso-
    phy," in The Relevance of Whitehead (edited by
    Ivor Leclerc), pp. 21-43.

_____. "Whitehead's Metaphysics," in Whitehead and
    the Modern World, pp. 25-41.

Hocking, W. E. "Whitehead as I Knew Him,: in Alfred
    North Whitehead: Essays on His Philosophy
    (edited by George L. Kline), pp. 7-17.

_____. "Whitehead on Mind and Nature," in The
    Philosophy of Alfred North Whitehead (edited by
    Paul Arthur Schilpp), pp. 381-404.

Hooper, S. E. "Whitehead's Philosophy: Space, Time and
    Things," Philosophy, XVIII (1943), 204-30.

Kuipers, A. "Model and Insight," in The Concept and the
Role of the Model in Mathematics and Natural
and Social Sciences, pp. 125-32.

de Laguna, T. "Point, Line, and Surface, as Sets of
Solids," The Journal of Philosophy, Vol. XIX,
No. 17 (1922), 449-61.

_____. Review of An Enquiry Concerning the Principles
of Natural Knowledge, by Alfred North Whitehead,
The Philosophical Review, XXIX (1920), 269-75.

Lawrence, Nathaniel. "Single Location, Simple Location,
and Misplaced Concreteness," The Review of Metaphysics, VII (1953-54), 225-47.

_____. "Whitehead's Method of Extensive Abstraction,"
Philosophy of Science, XVII (1950), 142-63.

Leclerc, Ivor. "Form and Actuality," in The Relevance of
Whitehead (edited by Ivor Leclerc), pp. 167-89.

_____. "Whitehead and the Problem of Extension,"
Alfred North Whitehead: Essays on His Philosophy
(edited by George L. Kline), pp. 117-23.

_____. "Whitehead's Philosophy," The Review of
Metaphysics, XI (1957), 68-93.

Lenzen, V. F. "Scientific Ideas and Experience,"
University of California Publications--Philosophy,
Vol. VIII, 175-89.

Lowe, Victor. "The Concept of Experience in Whitehead's
Metaphysics," in Alfred North Whitehead: Essays
on His Philosophy (edited by George L. Kline),
pp. 124-33.

_____. "The Development of Whitehead's Philosophy,"
in The Philosophy of Alfred North Whitehead
(edited by Paul Arthur Schilpp), pp. 15-124.

_____. "The Influence of Bergson, James and Alexander
on Whitehead," Journal of the History of Ideas,
X (1949), 267-96.

_____. "Whitehead's Philosophy of Science," in
Whitehead and the Modern World, pp. 3-24.

MacColl, H. Review of A Treatise on Universal Algebra
by A. N. Whitehead, Mind, Vol. VIII (1899),
pp. 108-13.

Mays, Wolfe. "The Relevance of 'On Mathematical Concepts
of the Material World' to Whitehead's Philosophy,"
in The Relevance of Whitehead (edited by Ivor
Leclerc), pp. 235-60.

_____. "Whitehead's Theory of Abstraction," Pro-
ceedings of the Aristotelian Society, LII
(1951-52), 95-118.

McGilvary, Evander Bradley. "Space-Time, Simple Location,
and Prehension," in The Philosophy of Alfred North
Whitehead (edited by Paul Arthur Schilpp),
pp. 209-39.

Miller, David L. "Whitehead's Extensive Continuum,"
Philosophy of Science, XIII (1946), 144-49.

Miller, E. V. "The Emergence of Relativity in Alfred
North Whitehead's Philosophy," Australian Journal
of Psychology and Philosophy, Vol. I (1923),
256-67.

Murphy, A. "Ideas and Nature," University of California
Publications, Vol. VIII (1926), 193-213.

Norman, Ralph V., Jr. "Whitehead and 'Mathematicism,'"
in Alfred North Whitehead: Essays on His
Philosophy (edited by George L. Kline),
pp. 33-40.

Northrop, Filmer S. C. "Whitehead's Philosophy of
Science," in The Philosophy of Alfred North
Whitehead (edited by Paul Arthur Schilpp),
pp. 165-207.

O'Keefe, T. A. "Empiricism and Applied Mathematics in
the Natural Philosophy of Whitehead," The Modern
Schoolman, XXVIII (1951) : 267-89

Palter, Robert. "Philosophic Principles and Scientific
Theory," Philosophy of Science, XXIII (1956),
111-35.

187

_____. "The Place of Mathematics in Whitehead's Philosophy," in <u>Alfred North Whitehead: Essays on His Philosophy</u> (edited by George L. Kline), pp. 41-52.

_____. "Science and its History in the Philosophy of Whitehead," in <u>Process and Divinity</u> (edited by Reese and Freeman), pp. 41-52.

Ruvtinx, Jacques. "Alfred North Whitehead: une bibliographie," <u>Revue internationale de Philosophie</u>, LVI-LVII (1961), 267-77.

Suppes, Patrick. "A Comparison of the Meaning and Uses of Models in Mathematics and the Empirical Sciences," in <u>The Concept and Role of the Model in Mathematics and Natural and Social Sciences</u>, pp. 163-76.

Stebbing, L. Susan. "Mind and Nature in Prof. Whitehead's Philosophy," <u>Mind</u>, XXXIII (1924), 289-303.

Ushenko, A. P. "Einstein's Influence on Philosophy," in <u>Albert Einstein: Philosopher-Scientist</u> (edited by Paul Arthur Schilpp,) pp. 632-45.

_____. "A Note on Whitehead and Relativity," <u>Journal of Philosophy</u>, Vol. XLVII (1950), 100-02.

Wightman, William P. D. "Whitehead's Empiricism," in <u>The Relevance of Whitehead</u> (edited by Ivor Leclerc), pp. 333-50.

Unpublished Material

Bross, Helen H. "The Problem of Bifurcation in Whitehead's Philosophy of Science," Unpublished Ph.D. dissertation, Department of Philosophy, Yale University, 1952.

Felt, James W., S.J. "Whitehead's Early Theory of Scientific Objects." Unpublished Ph.D. dissertation, Department of Philosophy, St. Louis University, 1965.

Lackner, Vincent F. "Alfred North Whitehead's Conception of Scientific Method." Unpublished Ph.D. dissertation, Department of Philosophy, University of Toronto, 1962.

Molina, Fernando, R. "Whitehead's Realism in Relation to the Problem of Perception." Unpublished Ph.D. dissertation, Department of Philosophy, Yale University, 1959.

VITA

Janet Anne Fitzgerald was born in Woodside, New York on September 4, 1935.

She was awarded the B.A. degree in mathematics magna cum laude from St. John's University. A national Science Foundation Fellowship for Mathematics Teachers enabled her to gain the equivalent of an M.A. degree in mathematics. She was awarded the M.A. degree in Philosophy of Science from St. John's University in June, 1967 and the Ph.D. in December 1970.

Doctor Fitzgerald entered the Sisters of St. Dominic, Amityville, New York in 1953 and has taught for twenty-three years. She was appointed to the Philosophy Department of Molloy College in 1969 and assumed the chairmanship in 1971. She was elected President of Molloy College in 1972 and still holds that position. As President and Professor of Philosophy, Sister still teaches courses in philosophy of science, philosophy of mathematics, ethics, metaphysics, and contemporary philosophy.

Sister Janet has received many honors and was named the first Long Island woman "Achiever in the Field of Education." She is Vice President of the National Fellowship of Catholic Scholars, and serves on six boards of trustees.

191